World University Library

The World University Library is an international series
of books, each of which has been specially commissioned.
The authors are leading scientists and scholars from all over
the world who, in an age of increasing specialization, see the
need for a broad, up-to-date presentation of their subject.
The aim is to provide authoritative introductory books for
university students which will be of interest also to the general
reader. Publication of the series takes place in Britain,
France, Germany, Holland, Italy, Spain, Sweden and
the United States.

Hermann Flohn

Climate and Weather

Translated from the German
by B.V. de G.Walden

World University Library

McGraw-Hill Book Company
New York Toronto

Contents

Preface

There is hardly a more popular topic of conversation anywhere than the weather and its varying moods. There is always something to be said about the weather and it can safely be said in any company. Sometimes our remarks are made from irritation or relief – the weather might be too cold or it might be just right. But in some parts of the world talk of the weather is much more serious because its variations can be a matter of life and death.

Weather prophets and 'weather makers' have practised their arts for thousands of years. The ancient Greeks knew their weather signs, as we know, for example, from Theophrastus (380–285 BC). In these early times, weather was often associated with religious cults, and so we have the thunder-god Zeus and the Germanic god Thor. In the Old Testament, Jehovah appeared to Moses in a sand-storm, accompanied by flashes of lightning. In Britain, it was only a little time ago that a sixteenth-century law was revoked, requiring 'witches and weather prophets to be condemned to death'.

Even today there are many tribes to whom weather is still an act of the gods, and many of them are really quite expert at weather forecasting. The inhabitants of the Marshall Islands in the Pacific, for example, can recognise the characteristic high clouds, composed entirely of ice crystals, which precede a hurricane, and the symbol they use to indicate them is the same that is now internationally used for deep, towering, umbrella-shaped clouds. Among many peoples, rain magicians are simply clever observers who do not start their rituals until they recognise in the clouds the first signs of a storm.

Weather forecasting was until recently a largely empirical science based mainly on experience, and was somewhat haphazard. Recent developments in science and technology, however, are transforming meteorology from the empirical stage into a science based on a sound mathematical foundation – the physics of the atmosphere. I have therefore begun this book with the main principles of the physics of the atmosphere, even though this is for the beginner the most difficult part of meteorology to understand. But every attempt has been made to give an unmathematical treatment of the subject, and the few simple formulae given will suffice for our purposes. Once these main principles have been described, it is possible to lead on to the other aspects of climate and weather, and to describe the nature and scope of today's problems in meteorology and the various ways in which they are viewed by specialists.

The last chapter shows how recent work opens up the fascinating possibility that we may at last be able to exercise some control over climate and weather. The world population explosion compels us to study these possibilities with the greatest care, and already this side of meteorology is losing its academic character and is becoming both a scientific and a political reality.

1 Radiation and the heat budget

1 Radiation and the heat budget

All weather phenomena such as wind and storms, clouds, rain and snow, and all the energy changes associated with them, are the result of two basic occurrences in the solar system: the constant radiation of energy by the sun, and the 24-hour rotation of the earth about its own axis with its 12-month circuit around the sun.

The sun, an atomic furnace of enormous size, constantly emits intense radiation, amounting to $5 \cdot 2 \times 10^{24}$ kilo-calories a minute or $6 \cdot 15$ kilowatts per cm^2 of its surface area. But only a minute fraction of this radiation reaches the earth 150 million kilometres away. This minute fraction consists of about $0 \cdot 45 \times 10^{-9}$, or half a billionth of the total energy radiated by the sun. This is equivalent to energy from the sun striking the earth perpendicularly at the rate of almost 2 gram-calories a minute, or about $1 \cdot 4$ kilowatts per m^2, setting aside the amount absorbed by the atmosphere. But since sufficient data for the total radiation from the sun as measured by artificial earth satellites are not yet available, and the absorption of energy in the upper layers of the atmosphere, as measured from the earth, is known only approximately, the value of this basic figure is accurate only to about $\pm 4\%$.

Since the earth can be approximately described as a rotating sphere, the incoming radiation, which is known as the *solar constant*, is distributed over the whole of its surface (area of sphere $= 4\pi r^2$, where r = radius of earth), which is four times as great as its cross-section area (πr^2). Thus over 24 hours every square centimetre of the earth's surface receives on average almost exactly $0 \cdot 5$ gm cals/minute, a total of 720 gram calories. The unit commonly used to describe the amount of this radiation energy per unit surface area is 1 Langley, which is 1 gram-calorie per cm^2. The average radiation falling on a horizontal surface at the upper limit of the atmosphere is about 720 Langleys a day (Ly/d) or 349 watts per m^2. (The conversion factor is: 1 Ly/min $= 697 \cdot 35$ watts/m^2.)

If we call the solar constant S_0, then the amount of radiation falling on an area of any given inclination – a horizontal area is the

1 Insolation **S** of the sun
(S_0 = solar constant) as a function
of the height of the sun or the
zenithal distance : $z = 90° - h$.

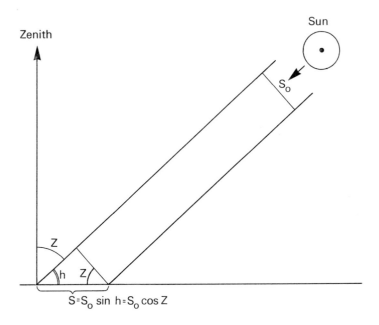

simplest example – depends only on the elevation of the sun (h) (or, zenith angle, z, $= 90° - h$; figure 1).

Calculating the total amount of radiation falling on to a horizontal area in the course of one day is therefore an elementary problem of geometry. But, because of the inclination of the earth's axis to the plane of its orbit, the so-called 'obliquity of the ecliptic', the total amount of radiation depends on the season of the year and the terrestrial latitude (ϕ).

The fact that the orbit of the earth round the sun is an ellipse with the sun at one focus must also be taken into account. The earth passes through the point nearest the sun (the perihelion) at the beginning of January and through the point farthest from the sun (the aphelion) at the beginning of July. During the respective summer months, therefore, the Northern Hemisphere receives less radiation than the Southern Hemisphere. S_0 varies, according to season, between 2·06 Ly/min in January and 1·94 Ly/min in July.

Figure 2 shows that the 'extraterrestrial' incoming radiation is a function of latitude and season of the year calculated for a horizontal area on the upper surface of the earth's atmosphere. In the two extreme seasons, summer and winter, the increasing length of the day in the polar latitudes outweighs the effect of the decreasing height of the midday sun in those regions. For this reason we find that the maximum daily incoming radiation figures are obtained during the polar summer – 1,185 Ly/d at the South Pole, and 1,110 Ly/d at the North Pole.

In the tropics, given approximately the same length of daylight of 12 hours, the maximum occurs when the midday sun is practically at its zenith ($z = 0$) and for this reason it varies with the season of the year between the latitudes 23·5° north and south of the equator. The minimum and maximum figures vary at the equator between 814 and 924 Ly/day.

The radiation emitted by the sun covers a broad range of the electromagnetic spectrum. As one would expect from a body radiating at about 5,700°C, about 45% falls in the visible portion of the spectrum with wavelengths between 0·4 and 0·74 microns (one micron is 1 millionth of a metre and is given the symbol µ). 16% of S_0 is absorbed directly by the atmosphere. This includes all the ultra-violet radiation below 0·29 microns which is absorbed by ozone (O_3), and much of the infra-red heat radiation between 0·7 and 16µ, which is absorbed by water-vapour (H_2O) and carbon dioxide (CO_2).

The atmosphere consists mainly of nitrogen and oxygen, some argon, and a number of other gases in very small quantities, together with varying amounts of water-vapour. In a dry atmosphere the proportion by volume of nitrogen is 78·1%, that of oxygen 20·9%, that of argon 0·9%, and that of the other gases 0·1%. From the point of view of the radiation budget, however, only three gases, present in very small amounts, play a significant role. These are carbon dioxide (0·03%), ozone (3 × 10^{-6}%), and water-vapour in greatly varying amounts.

If the atmosphere were of uniform density, instead of one whose density decreases with height, its height would be almost exactly 8,000 metres. Under those conditions, the layer of carbon dioxide would be 240 cm high, and the layer of ozone only 3 mm high. The total amount of water-vapour condensed to water would be a layer 2·4 cm high, varying from about 0·1 cm in the polar regions to more than 5 cm in the tropics.

The sun also emits energy in the far ultra-violet range in the form of X-rays of a wavelength of about 0·001μ and in the form of high energy particles such as protons, neutrons, and cosmic rays. However, these forms of radiation, which are subject to considerable variation, represent less than 10^{-5} of the total energy emitted by the sun.

The total energy emitted by the sun seems to change very little with time, but this needs to be verified by accurate measurements taken over a large number of years with the help of artificial satellites. But even considered over a geological time period of about a million years, indirect evidence indicates that the variation of the 'solar constant' is not more than a few per cent.

To reach the earth the sun's radiation has to pass through the whole atmosphere with all its haze and clouds, and suffers considerable loss in the process. This loss is due to absorption by the molecules of the air, and to scattering in all directions by haze particles. Such scattering is particularly marked in the zones of the tropics, subtropics and adjoining regions which are rich in radiation and where the dense haze layer is 3–4 km thick. The layer of haze scatters on average 18% of the extra-terrestrial incoming radiation. Of this amount, however, only 11% reaches the earth, while 7% is scattered back into space (figure 4).

But even greater is the influence of the cloud blanket which constantly covers about half of the sky, although in varying

2 Extraterrestrial incoming radiation as a function of latitude and seasons. Values are calculated for a horizontal area on the upper surface of the earth's atmosphere. The units are langleys per day.

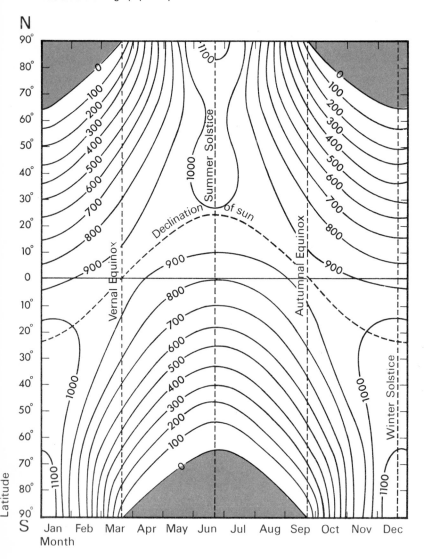

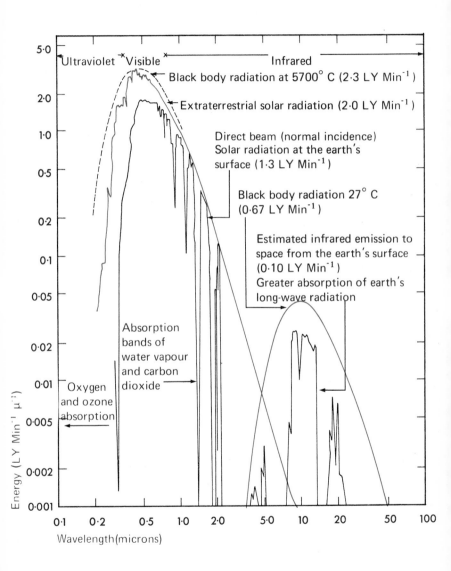

Energy (LY Min^{-1} μ^{-1})

Wavelength (microns)

density and at varying heights. The cloud blanket receives 40% of the incoming radiation of the sun. Of this amount, however, the larger part (24%) is immediately reflected into space; a small proportion (2%) is absorbed by water droplets and ice particles; and 14% is absorbed by the surface of the earth. This capacity of the upper surface of the clouds to reflect radiation is very high and is known as the *albedo*. Clouds, which consist of water droplets, and are often several kilometres thick, instantly reflect 75–80% of the radiation they receive; this, however, is not as much as the top layer of freshly fallen snow.

The amount of direct radiation 'S' reaching the surface of the earth is thus only about one quarter of the extraterrestrial incoming radiation S_0. The actual figure is 26% at any given time. To this, however, we must add the diffuse radiation from the sky 'H', partly scattered by dust particles (11%), and partly passing through the clouds which account for 14%. This amounts to 25%, which is almost equivalent to the amount of direct radiation from the sun.

The sum of the direct radiation from the sun and the radiation from the sky (S + H) is the largest item on the asset side of the radiation budget on the surface of the earth. It is known as the total radiation, or *global radiation* (51%). All radiation values are calculated for a horizontal surface.

The global radiation, however, is not completely absorbed by the surface of the earth because part of it is reflected, the amount varying with the surface albedo; for arable land the amount varies between 10 and 25%, depending on the nature of the soil and the growth stage of the vegetation; for dry savannahs or semi-deserts it is between 20 and 25% and for a bright sand-desert, up to 30%.

In contrast, the reflectivity of snow is extremely high: fresh snow usually reflects more than 80% and sometimes, as in the ice-caps of Greenland and Antarctica, more than 90% of the light falling on it. On the other hand the albedo of melting snow is only 40–50%, and that of snow-free sea ice only 30–40%.

The reflectivity of the surface of the sea depends on the elevation of the sun 'h'. When the sun is vertically above (h = 90°), it is only

4 The heat balance of the earth for solar radiation (see text for key).

17

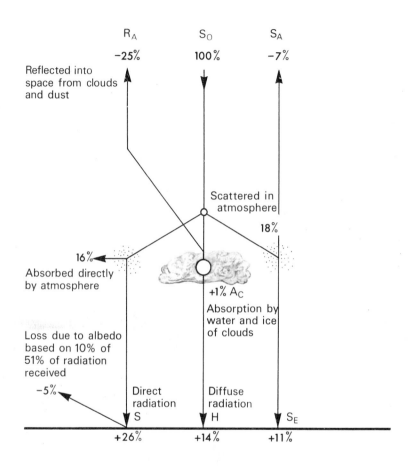

R_A S_O S_A

−25%   100%   −7%

Reflected into space from clouds and dust

Scattered in atmosphere

18%

16%

Absorbed directly by atmosphere

+1% A_C

Absorption by water and ice of clouds

Loss due to albedo based on 10% of 51% of radiation received

−5%

Direct radiation S

Diffuse radiation H

S_E

+26%   +14%   +11%

5 The heat budget of the earth for long-wave terrestrial radiation (see text for key).

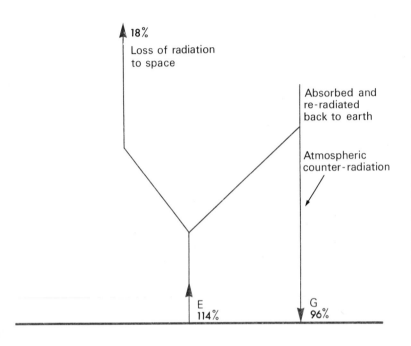

18%

Loss of radiation to space

Absorbed and re-radiated back to earth

Atmospheric counter-radiation

E 114%

G 96%

·4%, but as the sun sinks, this figure increases at first slowly and then rapidly to about 40% with an elevation of 5°. The average albedo of the surface of the sea in the lower latitudes ($\phi = 0$–30°) is only 5–6%, and 8–10% in medium latitudes, but in the higher latitudes in winter it rises to 15%. The average value of the albedo of the earth's surface can be taken as about 10%, in which case the *effective irradiation* of the earth's surface is $(S + H)(1-a)$, which on the average is 47% of the incoming extraterrestrial radiation.

These irradiation processes take place mostly in the visible and near infra-red portion of the spectrum and are balanced by corresponding emissions of long-wave infra-red radiation from the surface of the earth and the' atmosphere. The amount of this radiation depends on the temperature of the radiating surface which is between $+25°C$ and about $-50°C$ for clouds, and averages $+15°C$ for the earth. The maximum energy, therefore, lies in the infra-red region at a wavelength of about 10μ.

The emission of energy 'E' by the earth's surface averages 824 Ly/d, that is, about 114% of that of the extraterrestrial incoming radiation. Fortunately for the inhabitants of the earth the greater part of these long-wave radiations is absorbed by the lower layers of the atmosphere, and in particular by the water-vapour and carbon dioxide. These layers re-radiate energy and we call this long-wave, back-radiation of the atmosphere, which is directed towards the surface of the earth, '*atmospheric counter-radiation G*'. It has an average value of 692 Ly/d or 96% of the solar constant. From the physical viewpoint, the atmosphere acts like the windows of a greenhouse, which are transparent to the visible light, but absorb the outgoing long-wave radiation. Because of this to-and-fro radiation and re-radiation, the effective loss of energy E–G is only 114–96, that is, 18% of the solar constant, a figure which varies very little with the seasons and latitude.

We have now considered all the essential components of the *radiation balance* of the surface of the earth. The sum of these components provides the energy which is transformed into what we call weather and climate.

This radiation balance can be ascertained with the help of various instruments, but our present knowledge of its value is based mainly on an estimate of the distribution of its various single components, as well as on the determination of the value of the global radiation S+H at a large number of observatories.

The formula giving the relationship between the radiation balance Q – the difference between the effective incoming and outgoing radiation – is as follows:

$$Q = (S + H)(1 - a) - (E - G)$$

Estimates of the radiation budget based on the values determined

6 Radiation balance of the earth's surface in relation to latitude and season in langleys per day. (Data after M. I. Budyko 1963).

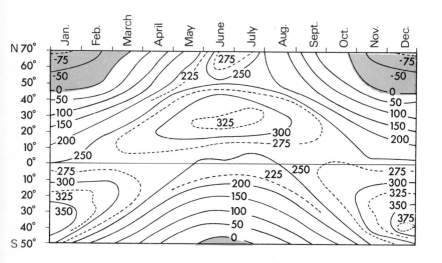

for the symbols of this equation have been made by a number of individual research workers and research teams. The figures obtained showed some slight differences, depending on the basis of calculation. Figure 6 shows the radiation balance at the surface of the earth, obtained from the new revised edition of the *Heat Balance Atlas* of M. I. Budyko and co-workers (Leningrad 1963). The global average value of Q, according to London (1957) is 212 Ly/day and according to Budyko (1963), 196 Ly/day. However, London's value refers to the Northern Hemisphere, whereas Budyko takes the value of S_0 as 685 Ly/day, a figure which was generally accepted until about 1954. Only about 29 % of the incoming solar radiation is therefore available for heating the atmosphere from the surface of the earth. Values of Q amount to 250–350 Ly/day in the tropics and subtropics, but figures naturally decrease progressively towards the poles. In polar regions the value of Q is lower than in the tropical zone, even in summer, because of the low elevation of the sun in the sky, which forces the solar radiation to take a longer path to traverse the atmosphere, and also because of high cloud amounts. In all seasons of the year, therefore, the values of the net radiation balance (Q) decrease towards the poles where they are actually negative in winter and in the annual average.

If we compare the values given in figure 2 with those in figure 6 we see the considerable influence the atmosphere with all its haze and cloud has on the amount of radiation available to heat the earth's surface, particularly in the higher latitudes. The special role of snow and ice will be discussed later.

Within the atmosphere it is various long-wave radiations which play by far the most important role. The absorption and emission of long-wave radiation – absorption of 'E', emission of 'G' – occurs principally in the lower 3–6 km of the atmosphere, the so-called lower troposphere, which is only a little colder than the surface of the earth.

The decrease in temperature with height that generally occurs in the troposphere is due to the fact that the long-wave radiation increases with height; an average 65% of the incoming solar radiation is re-radiated to space. Only a small portion of the upward long-wave radiation of the earth's surface passes unweakened through the atmosphere into space. Much of this is through the so-called water-vapour 'window' in the 8–12μ region of the spectrum. Measurements of the radiations passing through this window made with the help of the weather satellites *Tiros* and *Nimbus*, have provided detailed information on this phenomenon and on the temperature of the upper surfaces of the clouds and of the earth's surface.

In contrast to long-wave radiations, short-wave radiations traverse the atmosphere relatively unweakened, even though they are scattered by haze particles and the cloud droplets. The 16% of the solar constant which is absorbed by the atmosphere is mainly absorbed by the upper layers. Thus the absorption of ultra-violet radiation (with wavelengths less than $0.35μ$) by ozone causes high temperatures at heights of 50–60 km, with a maximum at what is known as the 'stratopause'. The amount of infra-red radiation absorbed by water-vapour and carbon dioxide need not be specified here.

We will revert to the layers of the atmosphere in chapter 3. If we take the value of the solar constant S_0 to be 100%, then the surface of the earth reflects about 4% of the incoming solar radiation, the atmospheric haze 7%, and the surface of the clouds 24%. The so-called '*planetary albedo*' of the earth-atmosphere system as it might be measured by an observer on the moon, has an overall value of about 35%; most of this is due to the reflectivity of the intensely white upper surfaces of the clouds. A first interpretation of the data obtained by the weather satellites already mentioned confirms very nearly the figure of 35%. It is interesting to know that the original figure was obtained by photometric interpretation of the so-called 'ash-grey moonlight', that is, the light from the part of the moon which lies in shadow, but is diffusely illuminated by reflected sunlight from the earth. Earlier estimates of the planetary albedo – this was before 1950 – were 42%, but this was certainly too high; the albedo of the surface of thin cloud is considerably less than that of clouds several kilometres thick.

If we take the planetary albedo to be 35%, then according to the Stefan – Boltzmann Law (which states that the amount of radiant energy is proportional to the fourth power of the absolute temperature) the long-wave radiation (65% of the solar constant) emitted into space by the system 'earth + atmosphere' corresponds to the radiation emitted by a body at a surface temperature of about —23°C. This shows that the major portion of the long-wave heat re-radiated into space is produced by the water-vapour and the upper surface of clouds in the middle atmosphere.

The atmosphere as a whole acts like a steam engine: heating is effected at high pressure on the surface of the ground and cooling at low pressure in the middle troposphere. Work is produced by exploitation of the temperature difference between these two points.

If we imagine the earth to be a planet with a homogeneous

surface and, like the moon, existing in a vacuum, and we then apply Stefan – Boltzmann's Law, taking the solar constant as 2 Ly/min, we obtain the following mean global surface temperatures when there is radiation equilibrium. For a completely water-covered globe with an albedo of 5%, this temperature is +4°; for a completely ice-covered globe with an albedo of 20%, it is −8°C; for a snow-covered globe with an albedo of 80%, it is −86°C. A land-covered globe without an atmosphere but with an albedo of 9%, which is the mean value estimated for the earth's albedo today, would have an equilibrium temperature of −3°C; this may be compared with the earth's mean temperature of +15°C which is due to the protective properties of the atmosphere. However, this does not take account of the great differences which may exist between day and night temperatures on a globe like the moon, for instance. The figures given are annual averages covering the whole globe.

The energy made available by the radiation budget is utilised for heating land and air, for evaporating water, and for various other processes. For the sake of convenience we include all the processes involved in one concept which we call the *heat budget*, and for added clarity we express this in the form of the equation shown below:

$$Q = T_B + T_L + T_V + T_S + T_N + T_R + T_{Biol}$$

Q is the radiation balance, while the symbols on the right-hand side of the equation represent the following:

T_B = Heat transmission into land masses (or T_M = heat transmission into the sea)

T_L = Heat for direct warming of the air (sensible heat)

T_V = Heat transmission to the air by evaporation (latent heat of water-vapour)

T_S = Heat for melting ice and snow

T_N = Heat used to warm precipitation as it falls

T_R = Heat generated by wind friction with the ground

T_{Biol} = Energy used in biological processes

The last three components are quantitatively insignificant but

7 Mean annual solar radiation in kilolangleys per year on a horizontal surface at ground level.

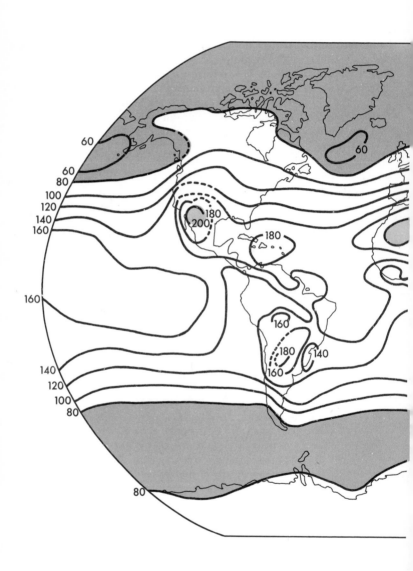

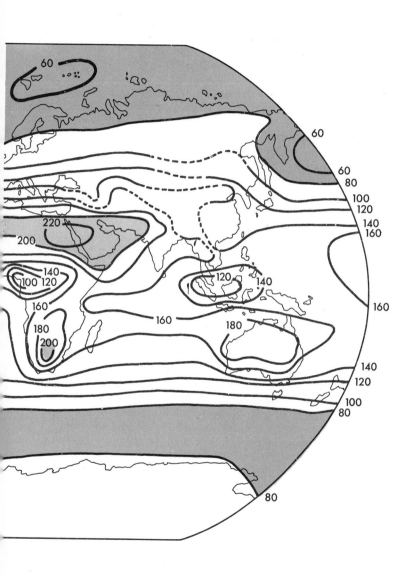

have been included for the sake of completeness. At the most, T_N has some little significance in the tropics where heavy showers with large cold rain drops and sometimes even hail fall on to the surface of the earth from the middle troposphere. If we assume that an average daily rainfall of 10 mm reaches the earth at a temperature of $+15°C$, the amount of energy required to heat it to the average ground temperature of 27°C is only 1·2 Ly/d.

T_R is the average work done by the atmosphere over the whole globe. This comes to about 2 watts per square metre, or 0·7% of the solar constant. T_{Biol} is of fundamental importance to all organisms, and therefore to man. It includes all the photo-biological processes involved in the growth of living matter, and also the heat given off during decomposition, as well as during respiration. Reliable figures for this are not yet available, but a number of estimates exist. In Denmark the average figure for vegetation during the growth season is claimed to be 375 Ly, which is about 2 Ly/day, or about 1% of the summer heat balance. For tropical forests the figure is 3·3 Ly/day over the whole year. The energy used in the metabolism of human beings and warm-blooded animals in a large industrial city in England is estimated at 4 Ly/day, but of course this is of local significance only. In any case these figures represent a little above 1% of the total amount of available radiant energy.

However, we must not forget that all sources of energy on earth are in fact stored solar energy. The potential energy of water power is the result of evaporation and the transport of water-vapour in the atmosphere. Coal and oil, also stored solar energy, are fossilised remains of the result of T_{Biol} in the early history of the world.

The amount of heat liberated in winter by the heating of large cities and industrial districts is estimated at 10 to 100 Ly/day. The figure for Sheffield, England in 1952 was 36 Ly/day.

The largest factors in the right-hand side of our equation are the first three – transmission of heat into land masses, sea or air, which includes the heat used during the evaporation of water or the melting of ice and snow. To evaporate one gram of water at 0°C we require 597 gram-calories but at 30°C only 580 gram-calories. To melt one gram of ice, which corresponds to a 10–12 cm layer of freshly fallen loose snow, we require 80 gram-calories. (Incidentally, 1 gram of water per square centimetre corresponds to a layer of water 1 cm high or a precipitation of 10 mm).

The heat used to evaporate water remains in the water-vapour molecule as 'latent heat', which is liberated when the water-vapour condenses again, as when clouds and fog are formed. This liberation of latent heat is one of the most important sources of energy in the free atmosphere.

The heat transmission into land masses (T_B) can be determined without difficulty for it depends on the conductivity of the ground and the intensity of the temperature gradient. In winter and autumn the ground is warmer than the overlying air by night and it gives up some of the heat it has stored during the day or during the summer months. During winter and autumn temperature increases with depth. In spring and summer, however, temperature decreases with depth. The slope of the temperature gradient, easily determined with ground thermometers, determines the direction of the heat flow T_B. Its value depends on the conductivity of the ground; for granite this is 0·01 gram-calories per degree (temperature gradient) per cm per second; for loose sandy soil the figure is 0·0005, and for fresh snow 0·0002, as compared with a figure of 1 for silver.

The very low conductivity of loose soil and snow makes each of them an excellent heat insulation layer. The daily variations of the temperature in such soil usually cease below a depth of 50–100 cm and in fresh snow they cease only a few centimetres below the surface; in both, the heat flow is very small, and can normally be ignored in calculating the total heat balance (unless these daily variations are specifically being studied). We can also justifiably ignore the permanent *effective heat flow* from the earth's interior, which on global average amounts to only 0·12 Ly/day and therefore contributes less than one unit per thousand to the heat balance. Locally, however, this figure can increase from 10 to 50 times; for instance, the heat flow through the ocean rifts, and in the volcanic regions of Italy, New Zealand, Japan and Iceland, where the heat from the interior of the earth produces energy on a vast scale. On the other hand, the heat produced by sources in the universe other than the sun, that is, re-emission of radiation from the moon and the overall radiation of distant stars, is many orders of magnitude less than the heat flow from the interior of the earth.

Heat flow in the sea is quite different from that on land. Although the conductivity of stagnant water is only 0·0014 gram-calories/degree/cm/sec, the sea, unlike shallow inland waters, is never still. The turbulent heat exchange in water is produced mainly by the wind and varies from 1 to 1,000 gram-calories/degree/cm/sec. The average may be about 300, or five orders of magnitude (10^5) greater than molecular conductivity.

Differences between day and night temperatures are hardly noticeable on the surface of the sea as the heat is distributed by turbulence over a depth of 100 metres or more. Differences between summer and winter, however, are highly effective, due to the great volume (and thermal capacity) of the oceanic reservoir. Moreover, since the oceans are kept in constant movement by powerful currents, horizontal heat transport plays an important role in the heat budget of many areas and particularly subpolar and polar latitudes. These currents are mainly wind-driven at the surface, while at greater depths the energy is provided by differences in density determined by the temperature and salt content of the sea water.

The transport of heat by ocean currents goes on throughout the year, mostly in the same direction and across vast distances. The Gulf Stream is of course one of the most well-known examples. Throughout the year it transports an astonishingly large quantity of heat from the Gulf of Mexico and the American east coast to the coastal waters of western Europe, and to the Arctic seas. The unusually favourable climate in regions served by the Gulf Stream is illustrated particularly well by comparing the winter temperatures

8 Isanomalies of temperature for January (*top*) and for July *(bottom)*. Values 4°C below the latitudinal mean are shown in blue and more than 4°C above the latitudinal mean are shown in red. Principal anomalies are in the Northern Hemisphere in winter, being positive over the oceans, especially in their eastern positions, and negative over the continents.

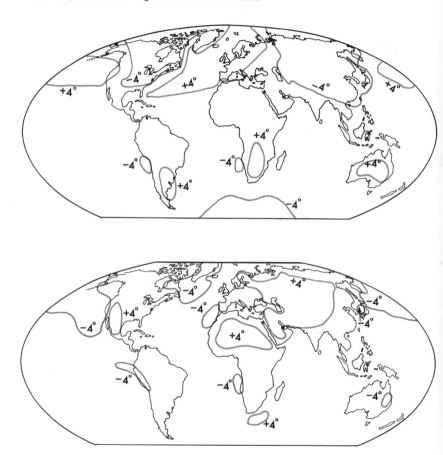

of northern Norway with the average for its latitude, where temperatures can be as much as 28°C higher.

East of Baltimore, the Gulf Stream gives off an annual average of 100–120 kilo-calories per square centimetre, that is, 275–330 Ly/day, which is even more than the net radiation balance in the tropics. In Iceland the figure is still as high as 180 Ly/day, and even near Newfoundland, where icebergs brought by the east Greenland current melt, the sea still transmits heat to the air. The oceans' primary warm currents pick up their heat energy from the intense radiation in tropical areas, where the heat transmission into the sea is 100–150 Ly/day.

The importance of the oceanic heat reservoir is demonstrated clearly on the east coast of America, and perhaps even more strikingly in the Sea of Japan off eastern Asia, where, in winter, extremely cold continental air regularly passes over large areas of warm, open water. This also happens in early winter near to the Great Lakes of North America and the Siberian Lake Baikal before they freeze up (an event which is rare before the beginning of January). Heat budget calculations show that seas with a temperature of up to +10°C transmit 900–1,200 Ly/day to cold continental air passing over them at or below −30°C. When this happens heat exchanges between the warm sea surfaces and the cold air above involve more energy than the solar radiation on a horizontal area at the upper limit of the atmosphere! In most areas the direction of the transfer varies with the season.

Thus the ocean with all its adjacent seas acts as a gigantic *heat reservoir*, absorbing heat in spring and summer, and transmitting it in autumn and winter, with a system of powerful currents ensuring a highly effective exchange and distribution of heat. The same thing happens, to a lesser extent, in the great inland lakes such as Lake Baikal, which releases from October to December on average 516 Ly/day, which is more than the global radiation throughout the month of June. This phenomenon always produces a decrease in the diurnal and annual range of temperature and a lag in the times of maximum and minimum temperatures.

Finally we must consider the particular role played by *snow* and *ice* in the heat budget – the factor T_S in our equation. Fresh snow reflects 80–90 % of the short-wave radiation falling upon it. This means that so long as the snow covering remains intact, the intense summer radiation in polar areas can have hardly any effect on it. Moreover, while a snow surface is particularly effective in reflecting radiation in the short-wave part of the spectrum, the numerous air pockets between the ice crystals also cause it to cool rapidly by emitting long-wave radiation at the surface, sometimes by as much as 15–20°C or more in a single night, if conditions are favourable. Paradoxical as it may sound, snow is one of the best (black body) radiators known. The unusually low thermal conductivity of snow confines the heat exchanges to a thin upper layer, and protects the ground below it by acting as a heat insulator, rather like the plastic-foam materials which are used to insulate buildings.

To estimate the value of T_S, Shumskij assumed that the snow cover which melts every year amounts in the Northern Hemisphere alone to 37 million square kilometres with a mass of 11×10^{18} grams, that is, about 30 gm/square centimetre. To melt this snow cover, no less than 2,400 Ly are required over a period of a few weeks. The result of the great consumption of energy during the thawing period is that the air temperature can rise only a little above 0°C.

Quantitatively, the most important factors in the heat budget are the exchanges of *sensible heat* and *latent heat* (of water-vapour), that is to say, the factors T_L and T_V of our equation.

The accurate measurement of these factors is the fundamental basis of all investigations concerning the heat balance budget. We cannot, however, discuss here in detail the methods which are used for this purpose, nor the theories on which they are based.

The exchange of heat between ground and air is effected by the vertical transfer of air, and therefore depends on its strength. We can express this more clearly, thanks to the classic work carried out by W. Schmidt in 1917, by using an exchange coefficient 'A' which tells us how many quanta of turbulence (tiny parcels of air travelling in one direction) pass upward or downward through a horizontal area, expressed in square centimetres, in one unit of time (1 second).

The turbulent or eddy transfer of sensible heat T_L is then the product of the exchange coefficient A, the vertical gradient of temperature and the specific heat of the air at constant pressure.

This vertical exchange coefficient varies considerably with time, depending upon the vertical temperature gradient and the wind velocity. When the ground surface is colder than the air, as is frequently the case in winter, air temperature increases and its density decreases with height through the first few tens or hundreds of feet. The layers of air are then said to be *stable* and the vertical air exchange is small (A = 0·1 to about 2 grams per cm per second). When the air is heated from the ground, which is what happens on most days because of *insolation*, temperature decreases and density may increase with height. The layer becomes *unstable* when the temperature decrease with height is faster than 1°/100 m and the exchange coefficient A rises to 10–100, and even to 1,000 in exceptional cases.

Vertical turbulent heat exchange, which is linked directly to air exchange by the exchange coefficient A, is 4 to 6 orders of magnitude greater than molecular conductivity of still air. The direction of the heat flow depends, of course, on the vertical temperature gradient. If the ground surface is colder than the air, then sensible heat is transferred downward from the air towards the ground. If, however, the air is colder than the ground, then the air is heated from the ground by turbulent or eddy heat transfer.

For the earth as a whole, the average heat transfer is upward. Thus on average, temperature decreases with height at a rate of about 4–5°C per kilometre in the lower troposphere, and about 6·5°C per kilometre in the middle and upper troposphere. However, over a snow field, at night, and often during the day too, heat transfer takes places in a downward direction, but because the air layers involved are stable, the amounts of energy involved are actually very small. In this case, temperature increases with height, in which case we speak of an 'inversion of temperature' or more simply an 'inversion'.

The accurate determination of the exchange coefficient or its closely related 'turbulent diffusion' coefficient is one of the most important and most controversial problems in atmospheric physics today. In the simplest case when the air layer involved is *neutral*, in other words, neither stable nor unstable, it can be determined directly from the rate of increase of wind velocity with height. The solution of the problem depends directly on the quantitative determination of the shear stress of the wind at the surface of the ground. In this connection we know, of course, that the surface friction coefficient increases with the roughness of the surface, the two extremes being represented by the figure for a smooth ice surface, and, at the other end of the scale, the figure for a broken forest of tall deciduous trees. Comprehensive measurements under almost ideal conditions in the treeless prairie of Nebraska have contributed considerably to the solution of these problems.

The turbulent transfer of latent heat, T_V, obeys the same laws as that for sensible heat and is measured by the product of the exchange coefficient A, the vertical gradient of water-vapour content (measured in grams of water-vapour per kilogram of moist air, and known as the specific humidity), and the latent heat of vapourisation. If we neglect the last of these three factors, the product of the coefficient A and the specific humidity gradient is identical to the evaporation V which maintains a constant upward flow of water-vapour from the evaporating water surface.

It is not difficult to determine the value of T_L and T_V, provided we make a number of simplifications, and are given a significant series of figures for the radiation balance Q, and the vertical wind, temperature and specific humidity gradients. We are then able to obtain a figure for the actual evaporation of any surface, whether covered with vegetation or not. This figure is one of the most important values in climatology, but it cannot be easily determined by instruments.

Most instruments measure the *potential* or possible evaporation where the water being evaporated is constantly replaced. But many such measurements are made in exposed positions where the wind velocity is too high or the temperature is too high because of radiation. The potential evaporation is identical with the actual evaporation only when there is no soil moisture deficit, as for instance in the case of open waters, swamps, and meadows above a liberal supply of ground water. In other cases, the actual evaporation is nearly always less than the potential evaporation. Once the soil moisture falls below a certain level, often defined by what is known as a 'root-constant', evaporation is severely reduced. But when there is plenty of water, evaporation reaches maximum potential values.

Overland, T_L and T_V are quantitatively the most important factors in the heat balance equation, for they use up the largest part of the energy made available by the radiation balance Q. Over the sea, however, this applies only to a limited extent, for there it is the storage and release of heat from the sea (T_M) which plays an important role and T_L is much smaller than T_V. According to the extensive calculations made by the Russian scientist, M. I. Budyko, the sea uses up, on a global average, 88% of the radiation balance Q for evaporation, leaving only 12% for the direct heating of the air. This also applies to the rainy, humid continents where the energy consumed in evaporation, T_V, is greater than the sum of all the other factors in the heat budget; in arid regions, on the other hand, where the potential evaporation is greater than the precipitation, and there is not sufficient ground water available to replace the water that has been evaporated, most of the radiant energy is used for the direct heating of the air.

Evaporation plays the main role in the overall heat budget since 71% of our globe is covered by sea water. There are two sets of values for this, obtained independently by J. London in 1957 with reference to the Northern Hemisphere and by M. I. Budyko in 1954 (revised in 1963) with reference to the whole globe, both the result of many years of study. The values they obtained show considerable differences. The most important of these relate to the albedo of the earth's surface and to the direct heating of the air (see table 1). Those not familiar with the unavoidable difficulties associated with heat balance calculations will no doubt be astonished at the discrepancies. But this is chiefly because random sample readings taken at a few points have to be extrapolated with the help of empirical formulae to include vast areas with greatly varying types of surface (type of vegetation, type of ground, etc.). When we do this we always have to ask ourselves two questions: 'to what extent are the original observations influenced by small errors in the experiment, and to what extent are they reliable and representative of the true facts?' The albedo values are based on a series of air-borne measurements whose accuracy is questionable since the results obtained in Canada and the USSR show appreciable differences. Extensive investigations to determine the values of T_L and T_V were carried out by the Russian workers, while London concentrated mainly on the complicated radiation processes within the atmosphere.

Our views on the radiation and heat budget of the earth-atmosphere system are closely related to another fundamental balance, namely, that of the water budget of our world. If we ignore all storage processes relating to ground water and the various types of ice, as well as to water from the interior of the earth and the cosmos, we find, taking the earth as a whole over a long period of a year or more, that there is an equilibrium between the evaporation V and the precipitation N. But this does not apply when we consider the oceans and continents separately, in which case we have to include the run-off 'R' from the continents.

With these simplifications the equations for the water budget may be expressed as follows:

$$\text{Earth (E)} \quad : \quad V_E = N_E$$
$$\text{Continents (K)} \quad : \quad N_K - V_K = R$$
$$\text{Sea (M)} \quad : \quad V_M = N_M + R$$

We know fairly accurately today the value of the precipitation

N_K and the drainage R from the continents. N_M, however, is difficult to measure on the sea because the wind causes unavoidable errors in observations made from a ship, and there is a little more precipitation on islands, and even on low-lying atolls, than on the surrounding seas. This additional amount of precipitation is caused by the increased mechanical turbulence and thermal uplift over these islands.

Accurate determination of the actual evaporation V over the sea is as difficult as it is over land. All instruments introduce slight but incalculable errors in the effects of wind and temperature. For these reasons it is extremely important that we should be able to determine evaporation independently through the global heat budget as mentioned above.

Systematic comparison of the results would then give us the hope of eventually obtaining an accurate value.

Unfortunately, we cannot comment here in detail on the figures given in table 1. We just have to accept their differences until they are clarified and meanwhile regard them as evidence of the uncertainty that surrounds the value of the factor V especially. Before it is finally obtained accurately, a large number of comparable measurements will have to be made with different instruments. This would have to be organised on an international scale. However we can say that global evaporation (V_E) is the largest consumer (T_V) of the available radiation energy (Q).

The alternation between precipitation and evaporation in the atmosphere takes place comparatively quickly. But since the total amount of water-vapour in the atmosphere is equivalent to a column of water only 2·4 cm high, this alternation must take place either 81/2·4, or 34 times, or else 100/2·4 or 42 times, in a year. This indicates that every molecule of water-vapour from the moment it is formed by evaporation from the surface of the earth to the moment it returns to it, spends on the average 9–11 days in the atmosphere. During this period it is usually carried by the wind over a distance of some 1,000 km. By contrast, a water-vapour molecule stays in the ocean about 4,000 years, and some 10,000

Table 1 Summary of the heat budget values for the Northern Hemisphere (London) and for the whole globe (Budyko)

	London 1957	Budyko 1954	Budyko 1963	
Extra-terrestrial solar radiation S_0	720	685	685	Ly/day
Atmosphere				
Absorption (short waves)	125	107	—	,,
Reflection R_0	254	274	—	,,
Planetary albedo R_0/S_0	35%	40%	—	
Earth's surface				
Global radiation $(S + H)$	371	353	356	,,
Albedo a	8·1%	14%	13·6%	
Effective incoming radiation $(S + H)(1 - a)$	341	304	306	,,
Effective outgoing radiation $(E - G)$	129	118	110	,,
Radiation balance Q	212	186	196	,,
Transfer of sensible heat T_L	78	33	35	,,
Transfer of latent heat T_V	134	153	162	,,
Global evaporation $V_E = N_E$	81	93	98(100)	cm/a

years in the masses of ice in Greenland and the Antarctic.

If we look again at our introductory survey of the heat and radiation budgets of the surface of the earth and the atmosphere, we can find some similarities between them and industrial processes. All the energy involved comes from an atomic furnace, the sun, where it is produced by the nuclear fusion of hydrogen to helium. The bulk of this radiation is equivalent in effect to an incandescent sphere of gas at a temperature of about 6,000° Kelvin, or 5,700°C.

This radiation is received by the earth 150 million km away, a pinhead in size compared with the vast distance involved. The earth is surrounded by a paper-thin envelope of air whose height (so far as 99% of the mass of the atmosphere between 1,013 and 10 mb is concerned) rises to about 32 km, that is, about 0·5% of the earth's radius (6,370 km). This envelope is virtually transparent to the light radiation of the sun, but comparatively opaque to the heat radiation from the earth.

The surface of the earth heats the air above it and evaporates water. Both processes require relatively little energy per unit area, yet they use nearly 30% of the available solar energy. If we regard the surface of the earth as a heating surface, and the atmosphere as the boiler of a gigantic steam engine, then the cooling surfaces lie in the middle and upper troposphere, where the greatest amount of heat is reflected back into space. All meteorological phenomena are caused by air circulation in the boiler of this steam engine. We will learn later how it works.

But however great the exchange between potential energy (air mass distribution) and kinetic energy (wind), gain and loss are almost balanced, except for the loss of energy caused by friction of the wind against rough ground surfaces, which produces heat. It may be a little confusing to the layman that we mention this small amount of heat produced by friction which accounts for 0·7% of the energy of the atmospheric engine, for its real energy is the sum of all the processes of transmission in the atmosphere, including the surface currents caused by wind on the seas. These processes of transmission also include the transfer of heat and water-vapour containing latent heat. When this heat is released sources of energy are formed which vary with time and place, but which can have a greater effect locally than primary solar radiation. Here our steam engine comparison begins to fall down. Our steam boiler is composed of hot and cold areas which constantly change their position and intensity. So while all our physical models are extremely useful when we wish to use modern mathematical techniques, there exists no model that can represent completely all the confusing and interconnected single processes that are involved. The energy changes may appear to be very small in themselves, but they occur everywhere over a vast area, and their sum results in a heat engine tremendous in size and performance, whose effect we can observe everywhere in the manifold variations of weather and climate. We shall study these effects in the following chapters.

2 Clouds and precipitation

2 Clouds and precipitation

The amount of water-vapour in the air varies with the time and place, and plays a very important role in the events that occur in the atmosphere. So long as there is no condensation, water-vapour behaves exactly like any other gas. But the atmosphere cannot hold an unlimited amount of water-vapour. The maximum possible amount it can hold depends entirely on temperature: the higher the temperature, the more water-vapour it can hold, until a point is reached where it is saturated. Immediately this maximum amount is exceeded at a given temperature, the air becomes supersaturated and condensation occurs. This means that the water-vapour is transformed into liquid water and the latent heat used once to evaporate it is released again.

Basically, the behaviour of the liquid phase in the atmosphere corresponds to that of a solution of a solid, such as sugar, in coffee or tea. Here also there is a limit which cannot be exceeded. If a saturated solution of coffee or tea is cooled, then the excess amount of sugar is precipitated in the form of solid crystals. A similar process occurs in the atmosphere: if air saturated with water-vapour is cooled, then the excess water-vapour condenses into water droplets.

A number of different units are used to indicate the water-vapour or moisture content of the atmosphere. The most usual of these is *vapour pressure*, that is, the partial pressure of the water-vapour, which is always a minute fraction of the pressure of the air. This always used to be expressed in terms of the height (in mm) of a column of mercury, but nowadays the most common unit is the millibar (mb). 1,000 mb being equivalent to a column of mercury 750·13 mm high.

Table 2 shows the relationship between the maximum possible or saturated vapour pressure, and the temperature. The actual vapour pressure of air is usually lower, since fog forms as soon as the saturation temperature is reached.

Another measure of water-vapour content is *relative humidity*, which is the ratio of the vapour pressure recorded to saturated vapour pressure. Other units are used for particular purposes, the simplest being the *absolute humidity*, or the *density*, of water-vapour expressed in grams of water per cubic metre. Since these units depend on air pressure, and consequently change with height, meteorologists today prefer the two units which are independent of air pressure: the *specific humidity*, and the similar *mixing ratio* of the amount of water-vapour to the amount of dry air, both amounts also being expressed in grams/kg.

The *dew-point* is the temperature at which the water-vapour present in the air at any given moment is sufficient to saturate it. If air at any given temperature with a relative humidity of, say, 50%, is cooled, the relative humidity increases until it has reached 100%. At this point fog forms and the temperature and the dew-point are identical. If the air is then cooled further, part of the condensed water must precipitate.

A phenomenon that occurs regularly in the atmosphere, but is only rarely encountered in the laboratory, is supercooling. Supercooling occurs when water remains liquid at temperatures below 0°C, a temperature at which ice melts rather than one at which water freezes. Table 2 shows that at temperatures below zero the saturated water-vapour pressure is markedly higher over water than over ice. Air that is saturated over ice is by no means saturated over water. This fact plays a fundamental role in the physics of clouds and precipitation.

But what are the causes of cooling in the atmosphere? They include:

1 Long-wave radiation during the evening and at night which causes a fall in ground and then air temperatures.
2 The rise of thermals (ascending parcels of air) and the expansion of air masses against the pressure of the surrounding air, processes which use up the internal heat energy of the air.
3 The ascent of airstreams over topographic barriers and over wedges of colder air nearer the ground, with similar expansion of the rising air.
4 The mixing of two layers of air at different temperatures.

Table 2 Saturation water-vapour pressure over water (E_w) and over ice (E_e) in millibars (mb)

Temperature	+50	+40	+30	+20	+10
E_w	123·4	73·8	42·4	23·4	12·3
E_e	—	—	—	—	—
E_e/E_w	—	—	—	—	—

Long-wave (terrestrial) radiation is given off by the surface of the earth and the resultant cooling is particularly intense where there is a large surface area in ratio to mass (and therefore to thermal capacity). For this reason, temperatures fall sharply in and above grass, roofs, etc. There is also radiation from and cooling of the haze particles in the atmosphere. Immediately the temperature of the air falls below the dew-point, moisture in the air condenses on cold surfaces, and dew forms on blades of grass, plants, roofs, and so on. At temperatures below zero, hoar frost make its appearance. The water condensed on haze particles in the atmosphere becomes visible as fog.

Cooling by the mixing of two air masses of different temperatures, for instance, in coastal regions, is usually limited to the immediate boundary zone between them. This usually results in hardly more than a thin fog with visibilities between 0·5 and 2 km when it occurs near the ground but it may form and thicken cloud along a boundary between two layers of air.

So far as weather is concerned, however, the most important type of cooling is caused by the ascent of air. If this is effected only

0	−10	−20	−30	−40	−50	°C
6·11	2·86	1·25	0·51	0·19	0·064	mb
6·11	2·60	1·03	0·38	0·13	0·039	mb
100	91	82	75	68	62	%

by the heat energy contained in the air, then we call it an *adiabatic uplift*, a process which takes place without any supply of heat from an external source. The process inside thermals is not, however, perfectly adiabatic because it mixes with the environment, particularly on its upper and lower sides. Nevertheless, it is often useful to assume adiabatic conditions where the temperature of the air decreases at the rate of almost exactly 10°C per km. As soon as saturation point is reached, fog or clouds, which are the same things, form, and higher still condensation releases the latent heat in water-vapour into the air. In consequence, the rate at which ascending clouds cool is not as much as 10°C per km, but about 5 to 7°C per km. We then speak of a saturated adiabatic process.

When air parcels descend, the reverse happens, and so there is a downward increase in temperature at a rate of 10°C per km. During this process, water droplets rapidly evaporate and the clouds dissipate. This partly explains the well-known Föhn effect. In crossing a mountain range, air masses sweep up the windward slopes of the mountains where, as soon as the temperature falls below the dew-point, thick cloud forms and precipitation occurs.

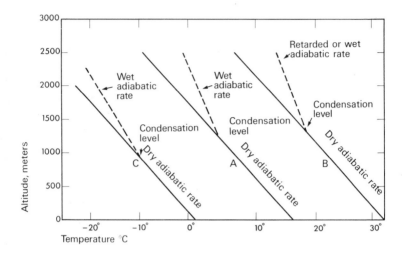

On the other side of the mountains, the air descends the leeward slopes and dry-adiabatic processes cause the temperature to rise. The temperature of the air is thus higher, altitude for altitude, on the leeward side of the mountain range than on its windward side.

Other factors also cause air to ascend and consequently to lose heat. Thus whenever air currents move toward one another, that is, converge, even if only a small force component is involved, the air with the lesser specific weight will rise and glide over the air with the greater specific weight. This type of uplift also leads to the formation of extensive cloud fields.

So long as the rate of vertical decrease in the temperature of the air is less than the slope of the adiabatic gradient in cloudless air, or the moist adiabatic gradient in cloud, the air layers in the atmosphere remain stable. Whatever the reason for its upward movement, ascending air becomes cooler and so heavier than the surrounding atmosphere; and its upward movement is therefore arrested. But if the slope of the vertical temperature gradient is steeper than the adiabatic or moist adiabatic gradient, then the

10 A diagrammatic representation of temperature changes which produce the Föhn effect.

47

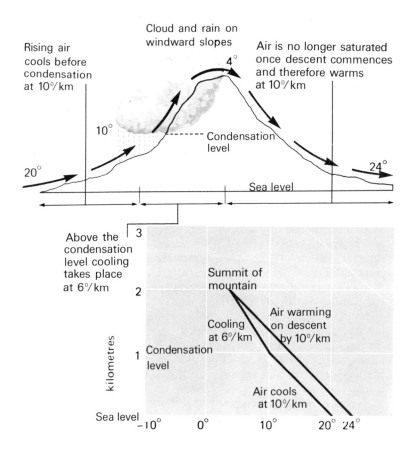

Rising air cools before condensation at 10°/km

Cloud and rain on windward slopes

Air is no longer saturated once descent commences and therefore warms at 10°/km

4°

10°

Condensation level

20°

24°

Sea level

Above the condensation level cooling takes place at 6°/km

3

2

Summit of mountain

Cooling at 6°/km

Air warming on descent by 10°/km

Condensation level

1

kilometres

Air cools at 10°/km

Sea level

−10°   0°   10°   20° 24°

11 Atmospheric stability and instability.
Instability prevails when the air becomes cooler
with height more quickly than the dry adiabatic
rate. The air is stable if the reverse is true.

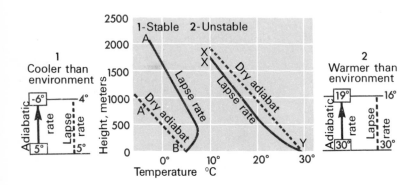

rising thermal always remains warmer and so lighter than its surroundings, and its ascent is therefore accelerated. The air layers are then said to be *unstable*. This occurs very often over land in summer, particularly in equatorial regions, where the uplift takes place not in a steady upward movement, but in a series of turbulent thermals ascending and descending side by side.

If saturation is reached at temperatures above 0°C, the water-vapour condenses into small droplets of water with a diameter of a few microns (initially about 2–10μ). These droplets in effect float in the air. But droplets of water form by condensation even at temperatures below 0°C, so long as the air does not contain what are known as freezing nuclei, which will be discussed later. It is usually only at temperatures below −12°C that ice crystals begin to form in any numbers; but supercooled drops in smaller or larger quantities occur at temperatures right down to −38°C. Below −38°C, which is known as the Schaefer Point, only ice crystals form, and they form spontaneously.

There are therefore three different types of cloud or fog: clouds composed entirely of water droplets which are known as *water clouds*; those composed entirely of ice crystals, which are known as *ice clouds*; and those composed of water droplets and ice crystals, which are known as *mixed clouds*. Water clouds can be

12 Cumulus clouds of different scale
above East Africa (Lake Nyasa at left),
frequently in rows parallel to the wind.
(3 September 1964).

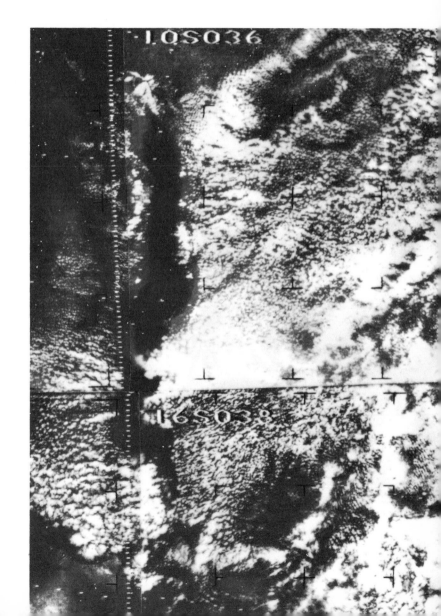

13 Cumulus clouds building up over Whernside, Yorkshire, England. Note the sharply defined boundaries of the clouds.

distinguished from ice clouds by their outward appearance, except in borderline cases. Their boundaries, particularly their vertical boundaries, are sharply defined, whereas ice clouds have a fibrous structure and their boundaries are usually ill-defined. When water clouds are sufficiently thick they cast shadows on to their lower layers, but this never occurs with ice clouds, at least in the middle and higher latitudes. There is a clear distinction between their effects on the appearance of the sun. Water clouds cause the phenomenon of the corona, a dull-coloured circle round the sun or moon, with bright edges and a diameter of 3–4°. This is sometimes accompanied by refraction effects. Ice clouds, on the other hand

14 Cirrus uncinus and some cirrocumulus, with their characteristic ill-defined boundaries.

cause various halo effects. The most important of these from our point of view are the two rings $22\frac{1}{2}°$ and $46°$ apart which are caused by refraction and reflection, and the so-called mock suns which mostly have a coloured, glowing appearance.

A third classification of clouds, which is particularly useful in routine observations of weather, is according to their height above the ground. The three main types are: low clouds, middle clouds, and high clouds. Low clouds are those that occur at heights up to about 2,500 metres; middle clouds, those between about 2,500 and 6,000 metres; and high clouds (generally ice clouds) those higher than about 6,000 metres above the ground. Naturally these classifications are only approximations which meteorologists use for convenience and some clouds will extend from 2,500 to over 6,000 metres.

We now have to combine two of our physical classifications – our division of clouds into water, ice, and mixed clouds, and our division of cloud layers into stable and unstable layers. The stable forms have the appearance of horizontal layers or sheets; they are homogeneous and extend over large areas. The unstable forms, on the other hand, have the appearance of adjacent bundles or cells separated from one another by gaps. There are, however, characteristic transition forms in which individual 'cells' are forced to spread out through contact with an inversion of temperature. Our classification of cloud forms therefore falls into nine categories or types, which are summarised in table 3. We owe the names of these cloud forms to Luke Howard, an English apothecary at the beginning of the nineteenth century. They were accepted partly because of their simplicity, but also because of the support they received from the German poet Johann Wolfgang Goethe in Weimar, who was an enthusiastic cloud watcher, perhaps because of his great sensitivity to weather changes. He mentioned these cloud forms in several of his poems, as well as in a guide to weather-watching which he wrote. The fact that the names of these cloud forms were in Latin also helped to give them international currency.

But how do we recognise individual cloud types? The best known of these are the simple layer clouds or *stratus*, which are uniformly light grey in appearance and sometimes spread over great distances. The stratus cloud, which has no structure, is identical with the extensive fog fields which occur near the ground in autumn and winter. Both originate in a similar way from the passage of cold air close to the ground or beneath an inversion; or from the passage of warm air over cold air layers or the ground. But even a thick widespread fog during the day still allows part of the solar radiation to pass through. This warms the ground and dissipates or thins out the fog close to it. The low-lying fog rises

Table 3 Classification of cloud forms

Physical

	Water clouds	Ice clouds	Mixed clouds
Moist stable	Stratus (S) Fog, High fog	Cirrostratus (Cs) Altostratus (As)	Nimbostratus (Ns)
Moist unstable	Cumulus (Cu) Fractocumulus (Fc) Fractostratus (Fs)	Cirrus (Ci)	Cumulonimbus (Cb) chaotic Ns, intermingled with buoyant thermals
Transition forms below inversions	Stratocumulus (Sc) Altocumulus (Ac)	Cirrocumulus (Cc)	

According to altitude

Low clouds (up to 2,500 m above the earth's surface) :
S, Sc, Cu, Fs, Fc
Middle clouds (2,500–6,000m) : Ac, As
High clouds (above 6,000m) : Ci, Cs, Cc
Clouds with vertical development : Ns, Cb

Summary of Latin terms: Stratus = layer ; cirrus = fibre ; nimbus = umbrella ;
cumulus = heap ; altus = high ; fractus = broken.

15 *Top* Stratus clouds over the mountains of Mull, Scotland.
16 *Bottom* Cumulus clouds produced by convection on Mull.
The wind was from left to right and convection began only
over the land surface. Upgrowth of the clouds was prevented by
an inversion associated with an anticyclone over England.

17 *Top* Cumulonimbus clouds showing
characteristic anvils at the tropopause, being
associated with unstable layers in the atmosphere.
18 *Bottom* Fractostratus clouds beneath the
general cloud base during heavy rain.

19 Lee waves in mountains. Behind the barrier there are strongly turbulent rotor clouds below and lee wave (altocumulus lenticularis) clouds at various heights above. (After Kuttner).

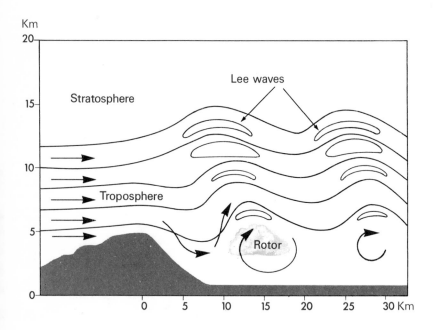

and becomes high fog at an altitude of 50–100 metres, where it persists for a little while.

Equally well known are the heaped clouds known as *cumulus*. Cumulus clouds develop individually during the day in strong radiation weather, forming first of all rather flattened spherical shapes with a diameter of several hectometres. These then swell into still larger shapes when the air layers are unstable and eventually form *cumulonimbus* (shower) clouds, which we will discuss later on. Over the sea the base of cumulus clouds usually lies at a height of 300–600 metres, and over land at 600–1,200 metres. But towards the end of long dry periods and in arid regions their height may be 2,500 metres and above. Small wisps of cloud are described by meteorologists as *fractocumulus* clouds. Similar

20 Orographic clouds over
southern Greece and the Aegean
Islands. At Euboea (*top*) is a dense
meso-scale cloud system.

57

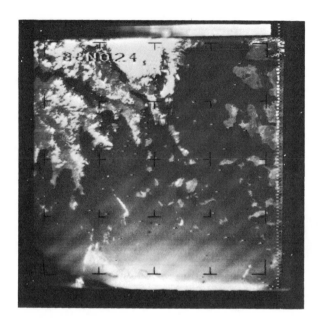

wisps of cloud form in the turbulent ground friction zone beneath a
widespread cloud cover during and after rain. They are called
fractostratus clouds.

In strong radiation weather the wisps of fractocumulus cloud
form extensive cloud fields which are first of all flat, but, later, if
they do not come in contact with an inversion, rapidly develop into
huge cloud piles, *cumulus congestus*, whose initial 'cauliflower'
heads constantly take on new shapes. From aeroplanes we can
see how these clouds sometimes form side by side, or one behind
the other, into rows and streets, and even into a series of networks
containing right angles. This 'organised convection' occurs frequently above tropical seas, and provides information about air currents.

All these cloud forms are typical of conditions when there are

21 *Below* Cumulus congestus clouds over the Vale of Evesham, England. These later developed to give the cumulonimbus clouds of figure 17.
22 *Right* An extensive sheet of stratocumulus cloud slightly broken up into small billows. There is an altostratus layer above.

moist unstable layers present in the atmosphere. In many cases these unstable layers are limited above by a warm layer forming an inversion which may act like an atmospheric lid as a barrier to rising thermals. When they encounter this inversion, the clouds begin to spread laterally, but the underlying unstable layer invariably leads to their breaking up into individual cells, bands or rolls which frequently form in long rows according to the direction of the wind. We call such clouds *stratocumulus* at low heights and *altocumulus* at middle heights. The transition between one form and another is very fluid and is recognised from the ground by a meteorological convention.

In upland regions one often sees long cigar-shaped or lens-shaped

(lenticular) clouds which are formed on the cool peaks of a vertically undulating air flow over hill ranges. When there are moist unstable layers in the middle troposphere, a characteristically unstable type of altocumulus cloud forms in eddying flakes (*altocumulus floccus*) or the billowing turret shapes (*altocumulus castellanus*) which precede thunderstorms. From nearby these billowing clouds can hardly be distinguished from billowing cumulus clouds, but ice particles form more readily in them.

All these cloud forms belong predominantly to the group of water clouds consisting of water droplets, whose edges are well defined. In contrast to these are the ice clouds, consisting of ice crystals, whose boundaries are blurred and fibrous. The *cirrostratus* cloud is a thin, veil-like layer of ice cloud through which the sun shines practically unhindered. However, when there is an increase of wind velocity with height and a systematic gliding of one layer over another, this type of cloud may become so dense that the sun can only just shine through it. In that case we speak of *altostratus* cloud which may become so dense that the sun is completely invisible through it. The thickness of such clouds is often 4–6 km, yet their lower boundary is hardly detectable. Flying through such cloud one often passes through an ice fog which gradually blurs out the contours of the surface of the earth until one finds oneself in the middle of the cloud layer. At the same time there is a colour change from the brilliant white of the cirrostratus layer to a dark lead-grey.

In the region of the highest ice clouds we often find a configuration of fibrous clouds or else spherical clouds with extended pennants (*cirrus*) which may indicate the presence of thermally unstable layering. In the last case (*cirrus uncinus*) we are really dealing with snow which, falling out of its mother cloud, is stretched out lengthways by the vertical shear force of the wind. More rare are the *cirrocumulus* clouds, small lens-shaped puffs which look *en masse* rather like small altocumulus clouds, but which have a typically silky sheen and the characteristic appearance of pure ice clouds. They often occur in conjunction

23 Altocumulus lenticularis over Taormina, Sicily, with Mount Etna at bottom left. Height about 3,050 metres. The wind was north-westerly, and these wave clouds were formed by the mountains of north-west Sicily.

with the lee waves of upland regions. Precipitation from the clouds we have discussed is rare, at least in middle and high latitudes, except for drizzle or light snowfall from low-lying stratus or stratocumulus clouds.

Mixed cloud systems, the third group of our classification, are quite different. They consist of ice particles and water droplets, and rise to considerable heights. In some typical cases they extend from some 300 metres above the ground, through the entire troposphere to the tropopause, with perhaps a few intermediate cloudless layers.

25 Thin cirrostratus cloud ahead of
a warm front, gradually thickening in the
distance with cumulus clouds beneath.

63

Mixed clouds are usually accompanied by considerable precipitation. The stable form is the *nimbostratus* cloud, colouring the sky uniformly dark grey and the precipitation falls as persistent rain or snow. However, the unstable type, *cumulonimbus*, is formed by huge volumes of billowing clouds towering higher and higher, and breaking through all barrier layers until they spread out at the tropopause in the shape of a gigantic ice umbrella or anvil (figure 17). These are typical shower clouds. Showers begin to form in our latitude the moment ice forms in the upper layers of a cloud. An

26 Altocumulus
castellanus
over Malta.

27 Dense altostratus with fractostratus at lower levels over the Pennines, England. Snow began falling within two hours associated with a warm front from the north-west on 6 January 1967.

attentive observer can actually see the formation of an ice veil or cap quite clearly. It is at this stage that the first, still rather weak, electric discharges generally occur, their electromagnetic waves interfering with radio reception in the middle- and long-wavebands by producing crackling noises (discharges). The bearings of these 'atmospheric disturbances' (often called 'atmospherics') may be determined from far away, and furnish meteorologists with information on shower and thunderstorm zones. In other areas dust storms are accompanied by similar electrical discharges. There is a gradual evolution (not yet fully understood) of shower clouds into a fully developed thunderstorm with lightning and

28 Dense nimbostratus over the Norwegian fjords producing heavy rain.

67

thunder. The precipitation takes the form of rainfall rapidly changing in volume and sometimes intermingled with sleet or hail.

An almost vertical zone of extremely powerful up-currents forms in the centre of thunderstorms. This zone, sometimes called a chimney or tower, has a diameter of about 100 metres and a vertical wind component in the higher levels of up to 30 m/second or 108 km/hour or more. Such chimneys sometimes break right through the tropopause, and penetrate with great force into the invariably stable stratosphere. The wind shear in these tower-like structures is enormous and for that reason pilots of civil aircraft avoid them as much as possible. The life of single towers is only

29 Model of the mature Cb-cell.
Commas=rain and drizzle;
stars=snow and ice;
arrows=wind currents.
(Modified from Byers 1949).

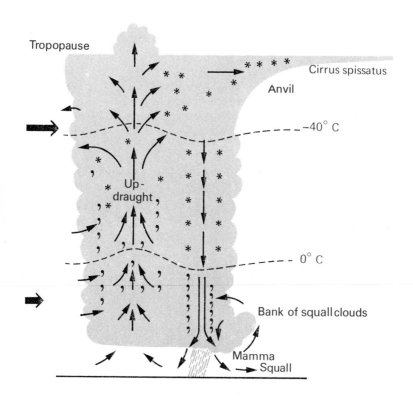

30–60 minutes, but they often amalgamate into huge organised systems which move only slowly with the surrounding currents and may persist for hours.

Stable and unstable forms of clouds often combine in such a way that the stable nimbostratus cloud is penetrated by cumulonimbus clouds with their characteristic umbrella-shaped forms, so that persistent rain occasionally gives way to heavy intermittent rain. Flying through such bad weather we leave the uniformly grey nimbostratus cloud and enter a chaotic cloud system in which cloud-free gaps are being filled by bubbling and billowing clouds accompanied by very strong turbulence. The observer on the ground finds it very difficult to distinguish this form of cloud from the stable nimbostratus cloud, and for that reason it does not have a name of its own. But a careful observer will notice the rapid variations in the volume of precipitation and in the light conditions associated with it.

If we study a typical water cloud carefully, we find that it is composed of a varying number of single droplets of varying sizes. The number of these droplets fluctuates around 500 per cubic centimetre. Their size also varies considerably, but most of them have a diameter of less than 5μ, that is, 5/1,000 th mm. The average diameter of these water droplets is appreciably increased after collisions with a small number of markedly larger drops. The liquid water content of such clouds is relatively small, usually amounting to less than 1 gram/m³ which is much less than the average water-vapour content of clouds, at least at temperatures above −10°C.

The mechanism by which these droplets or crystals are formed in clouds is by no means obvious. Certainly, many billions of water-vapour molecules must coalesce to form a single small water droplet and more than a million cloud droplets must combine to form each raindrop. Intensive investigations in laboratories and in field experiments have shown that the formation of water droplets occurs practically always on so-called condensation nuclei, small particles, usually slightly hygroscopic, which are normally present in the troposphere in large numbers, and attract the water-vapour molecules when the moisture content of the air is near saturation point. Only a small number of these nuclei are sea-salt nuclei as was once thought; most of them are the result of combustion processes; or else they are dust particles. In urban and industrial zones there are 10^5 to 10^6 nuclei per cm³, and elsewhere about 10^4 per cm³; even in the upper parts of the troposphere there are still a few hundred per cubic centimetre. This means that there are nearly always a sufficient number of nuclei available for the condensation process when the temperature falls below the dew-point.

The next question is more difficult: how do these small cloud droplets form precipitation? For even a droplet in very fine drizzle has a diameter of about 1/10th mm, and a typical raindrop, 1–2 mm. Several tens of thousand of cloud droplets (of average diameter 0·001 mm) must therefore coalesce before a drizzle drop is formed, and many million droplets before a large drop comes into being. The first attempt to find an answer to our question was made in 1933 by the Swedish meteorologist Tor Bergeron. He argued that rain consisting of large drops usually came from very deep clouds. It is a fact that in high latitudes heavier rain almost always comes from clouds which reach a height where temperatures are about −10°C or less. But in middle latitudes only a proportion of the total rainfall comes from such clouds, although they do account for most of the heavy or medium heavy falls. When the vapour pressure lies between the saturation vapour pressure of the two cloud components, water and ice, ice particles increase in size at the expense of water droplets, because the saturation vapour pressure above an ice particle is lower than that above a water droplet (table 2). If there is a considerable difference between these saturation vapour pressures, as when the temperature is between −10° and −20°C, this process takes place quite rapidly. Eventually the ice particles become so heavy that they fall out of the cloud and melt at temperatures above 0°. Rain consisting of large drops in the middle and higher latitudes is in most cases melted ice. At temperatures over 0°C, the large rain drops formed in this way can gather up smaller droplets and so grow even more quickly.

In middle latitudes, rain consisting of very small droplets, that is, drizzle, generally falls from layer clouds in which the temperature is above zero, which certainly excludes any ice phase in the precipitation process. In the tropics, particularly in the interior of continents, and also in the extensive trade wind regions, ice phases

30 Rime growth on the summit of Ingleborough, Yorkshire, England (700 metres). This frost-like deposit forms on the windward side of exposed objects by the impinging of supercooled fog particles at temperatures below freezing point. It thus grows straight into the wind.

in the precipitation process are far less frequent. Here heavy showers composed of large drops come from clouds whose temperatures certainly do not reach the zero centigrade level, which in the tropics lies on the average at an altitude of 4,800 metres.

It has been shown that in every such 'warm' cloud, there are a few larger water drops some of which have been formed around particularly hygroscopic nuclei such as sea-salt nuclei. Drops of this kind grow very quickly by collision and the accumulation of smaller drops in their fall through the cloud. Finally they become so big that they either fall out of the cloud or are distorted and fractured into smaller droplets by air resistance so that the process then starts again from the beginning. It can be shown that this coagulation and coalescence process has a physical significance only when the depth of a cloud is at least 2,000 m. Ice particles play a role in tropical clouds only when there are heavy thunderstorm showers during which the clouds rise to a height above 10 km and so reach the level of spontaneous glaciation (below $-38°C$). We can safely say that in the middle and higher latitudes, by far the largest part of the precipitation is due to the ice particle process in mixed clouds, whereas in the tropics the coalescence process in warm clouds plays a large role.

The formation of ice particles requires the presence of a particular type of nuclei, known as freezing nuclei. These are generally crystalline particles which are considerably less numerous in the atmosphere than condensation nuclei. Moreover, their number is subject to great variation. Some of these nuclei act at temperatures only a few degrees below zero, but it has been shown that the freezing process normally occurs at temperatures at least about $-12°C$ and preferably between $-30°C$ and $-38°C$. It obviously depends on the chemical constitution of the ice nuclei.

Ice crystals formed by gentle sublimation on to a nucleus are the most interesting, and at the same time, the most beautiful, shapes to be found in the atmosphere. Examined through a magnifying glass snow crystals are generally seen to be 6-pointed branched stars. But these snow stars represent only a few of the great variety of shapes of ice crystals found in the atmosphere. All these ice crystals have a hexagonal structure. They may be in the shape of hexagonal plates, or columns, or needles with hexagonal cross section. Such hexagonal shapes are also found in hoar frost on the cold surfaces of glass, grass blades, roofs, etc. Hoar frost crystals can sometimes be astonishingly beautiful. The dimensions of most crystals are about 1 mm, only the larger snow stars reaching 3–5 mm. In turbulent air currents these stars may cohere and so form extended large snow flakes with dimensions of several centimetres. Japanese scientists have carefully studied the conditions under which the various shapes of crystals form, both in the open air and in low-temperature laboratories. Their formation depends on temperature and relative humidity, and in particular on supersaturation with respect to ice. The higher altitude ice clouds, the cirrus clouds, are generally formed from very small needle-shaped crystals at temperatures around $-40°C$.

Of the constituents of precipitation, we have already considered large rain drops, as well as the much finer drizzle droplets. These, however, can also exist as supercooled rain at air temperatures below zero centigrade. This happens when at heights of say, 1,000–2,000 metres, a cloud layer with temperature above zero causes all the ice particles to melt. Supercooled rain freezes on contact with the ground and forms a dangerous coating of ice known as glazed frost. Sometimes this type of rain freezes in the air, in which case glassy ice granules are formed.

Soft hail, which is most common during showers in early spring, consists of an irregular agglomerate of many small needle-shaped crystals, which appear to be white because of the air they contain. If they fall through a layer of supercooled water droplets, they become coated with glassy ice and form graupel or *small hail*. These ice-coated graupel sometimes bounce into the air on striking the ground.

Since strong upward and downward movements can exist side by side in a shower cloud, it often happens that these ice granules are swept up to great heights and the process of accretion described above starts afresh. This is why a hailstone, which can have a diameter of several centimetres, often consists of a series of skins, rather like an onion. Hail usually falls from the centre of a shower cloud, the so-called 'hail tower', which has a diameter of about 1 km, but when such a cloud moves rapidly, it can cause damage in a strip extending over dozens of kilometres. In exceptional cases, a few hailstones may reach the size of a tennis ball, in which case the damage is done not only to vegetation, but also to greenhouses, window panes, roof tiles, and even the bonnets of automobiles and the sheet metal skin of aircraft. Today there is much less mystery surrounding the formation of these huge hailstones, which may consist of 8–10 successive 'onion skins', since the upward air velocities in the centre of hail towers have been measured with great accuracy and found to reach 30 m/second or more. With such velocities even large hailstones can not only be kept in suspension, but also carried upward. As a result, pilots of gliders have sometimes been subjected to a hailstone bombardment from below.

Our present ideas on the formation of precipitation in clouds are due basically to the investigation of Scandinavian, German, British and American meteorologists between 1933 and 1960. There are two basic processes: in supercooled water clouds or mixed clouds, the cloud components grow around ice crystals, whereas in warm clouds, that is, clouds in which the temperature is above zero centigrade, water drops grow by accumulating smaller drops. This knowledge may make it possible, at least in principle, to induce the process of precipitation artificially.

Our knowledge of the way in which precipitation is formed and distributed has increased considerably in the last decade, thanks to radar. Microwaves, with a wavelength of a few centimetres, are reflected by water drops and ice crystals in such a way that it is possible to represent on a radar screen the horizontal and vertical distribution of rain drops and ice crystals in space. The reflectivity depends on the sixth power of the radius of the droplet and on the wavelength. In the waveband between 3 and 10 cm it is the larger

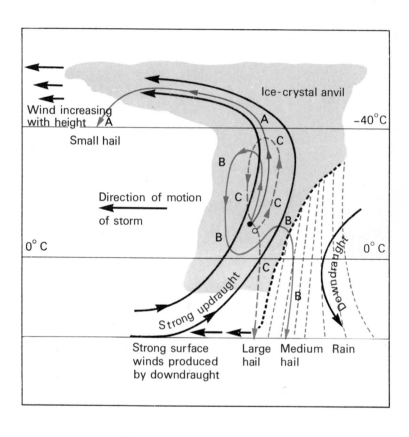

Ice-crystal anvil

−40°C

Wind increasing
with height

Small hail

A

A

C

B

Direction of motion

of storm

C

C

B

0°C

0°C

B

B

C

Strong updraught

Downdraught

Strong surface
winds produced
by downdraught

Large   Medium   Rain
hail   hail

32 Radar patterns of a light shower *(below)* and of a heavy shower *(right)*. The bright echoes show where rain is falling.

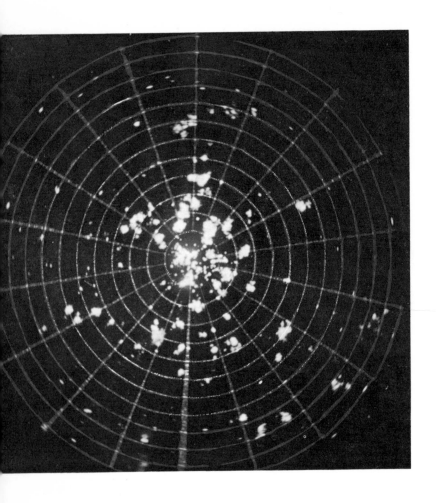

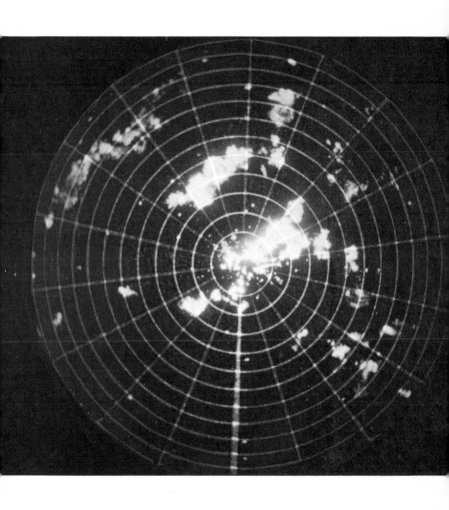

drops that predominantly reflect, whereas at wavelengths at about 1 cm, it is the smaller cloud components that reflect. With these instruments it is possible to obtain, at any given moment, the distribution in space of falling precipitation within a circular area around the radar station of a diameter of 100–200 km, isolated showers and thunderstorms giving particularly impressive pictures.

The constant growth and decay of individual precipitation cells and their movement with the wind, can be effectively recorded by time-lapse cine-photography. But the possibility of determining at the same time the intensity of the precipitation and its total quantity has not yet been fulfilled. Statistical treatment does not solve the problem. One of the chief causes of error is that when radar is used, the constituents of precipitation are assumed to be spherical, whereas they actually vary greatly in forms because of the effects of air resistance and wind. Another source of error is that radar waves are absorbed by falling precipitation.

3 Atmospheric layers and circulation

3 Atmospheric layers and circulation

Since the atmosphere is heated mainly from below it is obvious that its temperature will generally decrease with height. Near the ground, however, there are some exceptions to this basic law. For instance, radiation at night cools the ground and therefore the air immediately above the ground faster than it cools the atmosphere a little higher up, so that the temperature of the air increases with height and forms what is known as a *ground inversion*. Several similar effects occur in regions where snow and ice cause cooling: the high albedo of the snow cover in the spring and summer when radiation is strong and the large amount of heat consumed in the thawing of snow on land and ice on the sea.

All these factors produce inversions which reach to heights of 500–1,000 metres above sea level; in polar regions they occur throughout almost the whole year. They are often associated with widespread blankets of fog and mist filling the valleys and plains. Only a turbulent wind will mix the lower atmosphere and so destroy the ground inversion. In such cases the inversions are uplifted to altitudes of 1,000–2,000 metres, or even more (3–4 km) in the tropics and subtropics.

Such inversions can often be recognised by the occurrence of widespread stratus or stratocumulus cloud. They are often found in association with anticyclones (areas of high pressure). In tropical latitudes, for instance, there is often the so-called *trade wind inversion* at heights of 1,500 to 3,000 metres.

The hallmark of an inversion is the rapid decrease of density with height thereby producing that marked stability which reduces vertical exchanges to a minimum. The normal rate of decrease in temperature with height in the lower atmosphere is 3–5°C/km, but in the winter or at night there is often an increase of temperature with height and therefore a reversal of the normal direction of heat flow. In addition, in the middle troposphere, 3–8 km high, the temperature very often decreases with height at an average rate of 6–7°C/km, and above the subtropical continents the corresponding figures are 7–8°C/km. Transient inversions also occur in a boundary zone when warm air and cold air glide over one another.

The usual decrease of temperature with height was a fact already known at the end of the last century through observations made from mountain stations and balloons. But at that time it was thought this decrease of temperature continued to the upper boundary of the atmosphere where it reached $-273°C$ (absolute zero), the temperature of space. There was great surprise at the beginning of this century when the regular occurrence of an 'upper inversion' was discovered in middle latitudes at a height of 10–12 km and at temperatures between $-50°$ to $60°C$. Within days of each other in the spring of 1901, R. Assmann in Berlin and H. Teisserenc de Bort in Paris published evidence of this, based on measurements from balloons, and gave a tremendous impetus to the fast developing science of meteorology of the free atmosphere. Since then there have constantly been surprising new discoveries in the atmosphere, but at greater heights and in previously little explored zones. The meteorology of the free atmosphere is also known as *aerology*, from the Greek word 'aeros', meaning air, a word which could be more meaningfully applied to the whole physics of the atmosphere. The traditional term 'meteorology' goes back to the days of Aristotle, when all solid or liquid particles of air were known as 'meteors', ranging from meteorites to the 'hydrometeors' (rain, snow, hail) originating in our atmosphere. At one time a distinction was drawn between aerology and aeronomy, the latter being applied to the upper atmosphere, but this is no longer justified, since meteorology today, the physics of the atmosphere, is becoming more and more mathematical.

Proof that upper inversions occur all round the world, separating layers of completely different character, was obtained already in 1910 during a series of aerological expeditions in the tropics and in the polar regions. In the lower layer, that is the *troposphere*, temperature decreases with height as the result of the thorough mixing of the air caused by weather changes. The word 'troposphere' comes from the Greek word 'tropein', which means turning, or rotating, and 'sphairos' meaning a sphere. The upper layer, the layer above the troposphere, is the *stratosphere*, from the

82

33 Vertical structure of the atmosphere
to 400 km. All weather is concentrated
in the troposphere – the lowest 10–15 km.

Latin 'stratus', a layer, in which the temperature increases with height. The boundary between these two layers is known as the *tropopause*. The tropopause is often spoken of as the level of the first significant temperature minimum in the atmosphere's vertical structure, but in fact the tropopause is not a continuous surface and there is often an overlap and abrupt change in height between two quite separate tropopauses. We can see these tropopauses in single or multiple form when we fly over the Atlantic in a jet aircraft. They are identifiable by the thickening of haze, by the presence of cirrus veils, sometimes not more than 20–50 metres thick, and also by the incidence of slight or moderate turbulence. Above this the view in the stratosphere is in effect unlimited. We can see the reflection of the rising or setting sun which illuminates the cloud veils from below to a distance of 1,000 km, and we become aware of the marked curvature of the earth.

One or several tropopauses invariably exist in the layer between 8–13 km in the middle and higher latitudes. This is also the layer of the highest wind velocities, averaging 60–150 km/h. It is here, in long flat zones, that the centres of *jet streams* are normally found. Jet streams move at velocities far above 100 km/h, reaching in extreme cases 400 km/h, and even 500 km/h. Commercial jet aircraft today fly in this layer and even when they travel at an average speed of 800–900 km/h, jet streams play a decisive role as far as navigation, flying time, and convenience are concerned. Temperatures at these levels are between $-45°C$ and $-65°C$.

In tropical and subtropical latitudes the tropopause is found at a higher altitude of between 15–16 km, which is above the height normally used by civil aircraft. Here the temperature lies between $-70°$ and $-85°C$. In latitudes 25–40° there is an overlap between the tropical and mid-latitude tropopauses. Between these there is an interchange between the dry, almost moisture-free air from the polar stratosphere, and the more humid air from the tropical and subtropical troposphere. Studies with artificially radioactive particles have made it possible to estimate that in the course of 1–2 years all the air in the lower and middle stratosphere up to a

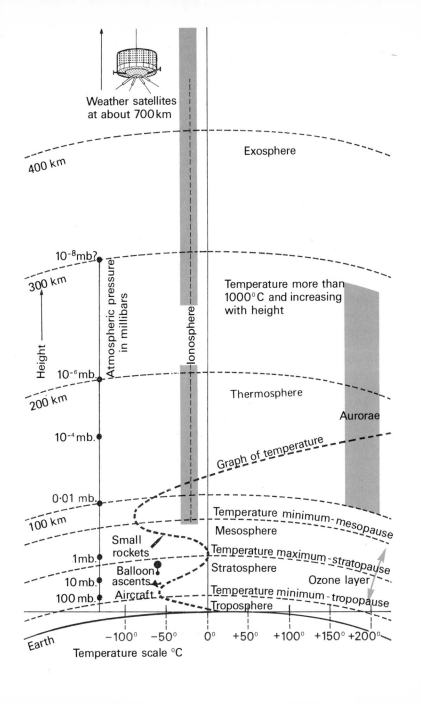

height of about 25 km is replaced by tropospheric air.

The troposphere is the real domain of the clouds, precipitation, and other meteorological phenomena. The stratosphere is almost free of clouds; it is also very pure, containing very few particles. The towering masses of ascending cloud in the troposphere spread out into shapes like huge anvils on reaching the tropopause, which also forms the upper limit of the extensive nimbostratus masses in bad weather zones. Only the powerful upward-surging air currents in the chimney with a diameter of some 100 m, in the centre of the high, towering cumulonimbus clouds have sufficient force to break into the invariably stable stratosphere, spreading out there in swelling shapes of roughly the same diameter.

The temperature in the stratosphere in the middle and higher latitudes at heights between 12–20 km is almost constant, but it then increases with height at the rate of 1–3°C per km. Over the higher lying tropical tropopause the rate of temperature increase with height is usually about 2–4°C per km. Temperatures at heights of about 25 km are almost everywhere −50° to −55°C with the exception of the polar regions, where differences in radiation and absorption result in a higher temperature, about −40°C in the summer, and a lower temperature, about −80°C, in the winter. This increase in temperature with height becomes particularly marked at heights above about 30–35 km. Above 50 km, however, temperatures normally range from 0° to +10°C, with the exception of temperatures above the two polar regions in winter. This maximum temperature corresponds to the upper boundary of the stratosphere, the so-called *stratopause* 50–60 km high. Sometimes there are several stratopauses, one above the other. The warmth of this layer is derived from photo-chemical processes that take place as the result of the absorption of solar ultra-violet radiation ($0 \cdot 2$–$0 \cdot 3\mu$) by ozone in the atmosphere. And it is here, at a height of about 55 km, that we find the upper limit of ozone concentration in the atmosphere.

Ozone is one of the trace gases in the atmosphere, there being only 1–3 molecules of ozone to 10^8 molecules of other gases, such

34 Cross-circulation and horizontal exchange (double arrows) in the region of the tropopause (thick line) and jet streams. (J_s = subtropical jet stream; J = polar front jet stream).

85

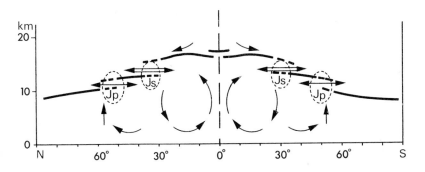

as nitrogen, oxygen, and carbon dioxide. But even this thin top layer of ozone suffices to form a second heating surface 50–60 km high, except above the winter poles. This information, available since 1950, seemed at first to be of only academic interest but the development of supersonic aircraft flying at speeds of 2,500–3,000 km/h, which is far above the speed of sound (1,075 km/h at −50°C), and at heights of between 20–25 km has compelled us to make a thorough study of the meteorological conditions in the whole of the stratosphere.

The air pressure at these heights is very low. If we take a ground air pressure of 1 bar or 1,000 mb, then the air pressure at a height of 5–6 km is 500 mb, with one half of the atmosphere already lying below us. On average, the air pressure at sea level is 1,013 mb, which corresponds to a column of mercury 76 cm high.

The polar tropopause and the layer in which wind velocities are at their maximum lie between the 300 and 200 mb (9–12 km) levels, but the height occasionally decreases poleward to below 8 km. On the other hand, the equatorial tropopause is at 100 mb, which is equivalent to about 16·5 km. At this height already 90% of the mass of the atmosphere lies below us, and at the 10 mb level (28–32 km) the figure is 99%. The pressure in the upper stratosphere, just below the stratopause at a height of 48–50 km, is only 1 mb. In normal aerological investigations, radio-sondes, carried by balloons filled with hydrogen, traverse all the layers of the atmosphere from the ground to 10 mb, and with special equipment even reach a height of 51 km or less than 1 mb.

The layer above, up to 60–70 km, is usually investigated today with the help of meteorological rockets. Above these heights the task is taken over by experimental rockets and satellites which are gathering increasingly valuable information. The results obtained show that above the stratopause, the temperature in the *mesosphere* decreases again very rapidly, and reaches a new minimum of —70° to —90°C in the *mesopause* at a height of 80–90 km, where the pressure sinks to a figure of about 10^{-6} bar or one microbar (μb).

Above the mesopause we come to something quite different. This is the *ionosphere*, which is also called the *thermosphere* or *chemosphere*, because of its thermal or chemical behaviour. Here the nitrogen and oxygen of the atmosphere interact with short-wave solar radiation and split into atoms and ions; they then absorb more short-wave ultra-violet radiation in the broad band of $0\cdot1$–200 nm (1 nanometre $= 10^{-9}$ metre). During this process the temperature rises to 200–300°C, and in the higher layers almost to 1,000°C. At the same time, because of the very low density of the air, which in the layers 5–10 km thick usually falls by one order of magnitude, the freedom of movement for a molecule becomes so great that the laws of the classic kinetic theory of gases as regards temperature no longer apply. Astronauts leaving their satellite at these heights must therefore wear heat-insulated clothes to protect themselves both against radiation from outer space and the long-wave radiation of the human body. Lack of space unfortunately prevents us from discussing the fundamental role played by this layer of atmospheric ions in the propagation of electromagnetic radio waves, and in communications in general, and describing its variations with latitude, seasons, and the activity of the sun.

We are not able to say exactly where the upper limit of the atmosphere lies as the density of the atmosphere decreases continuously with height. Above about 500 km, in the *exosphere*, there is continuous interaction between the atoms and molecules of the atmosphere with the micro-meteorites from space, as well as with the protons and neutrons from the sun. The interactions between the top layers of the atmosphere and solar radiation reach their maximum at a height of about 1,000 km and are visible from the ground as phenomena known as the *aurora borealis* or Northern Lights in the Northern Hemisphere, and *aurora australis* or Southern Lights in the Southern Hemisphere.

We see then that the vertical temperature distribution through the layers of the atmosphere shows two temperature maxima in addition to that at the earth's surface. First, the stratopause, 50–60 km up, in which the main activity is the photo-chemical synthesis of ozone from oxygen involving the absorption of near ultra-violet radiation from the sun. And, secondly, the thermosphere, above 110 km, where the force due to the density gradient reinforces the movement of electrically charged particles (ions) caused by the electromagnetic field of the earth.

The efficiency of these heating surfaces naturally depends on latitude and season. Together with the two cooling layers, one at the tropopause and the other at the mesopause, they form two circulation systems, one above the other. So far little is known about the upper circulation system which lies at 60–110 km; but its mass is certainly less than one-thousandth of the atmosphere, and its effect on the underlying layers, if any, is probably very small.

Heating under high pressure (below) and cooling under low pressure (above) are the basic characteristics of a heat engine, but they do not tell us anything about the direction of motion involved. When, however, the intensity of heating and cooling changes in a horizontal direction, say, according to latitude, then we do know the direction of movement. This basic principle of circulation is demonstrated by the changes of wind direction which differentiate *land* and *sea breezes*. As soon as the nocturnal ground inversion has dissipated, at about 2–3 hours after sunrise, the ground temperature rises. A lake, on the other hand, warms more slowly because of its higher albedo near sunrise and sunset, the

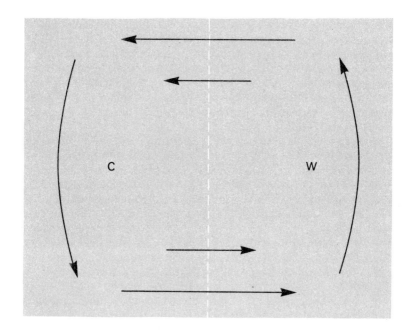

deeper penetration of solar radiation, the mixing of heat through a deep layer, and the heat used in evaporation. The lake and the air above it are therefore cooler by day than the land. This causes horizontal density and pressure gradients to form in opposite directions in the air near the surface and at a higher level and produces a circulation of air which we can simulate in a simple experiment.

Let us imagine a well heated room in the winter and an adjoining unheated cool ante-room. Now let us open the door between them just a little. At once we become aware of a draught whose direction we can determine with the help of a lighted candle. We see that low down, the direction of the draught is from the cool ante-room to the warm room, whereas high up it is in the opposite direction. In the middle there is a neutral zone in which the flame of the candle remains unaffected and burns vertically. This then is the simplest model of thermal circulation between a warm and a cold air column. Low down, the direction is from the cold to the warm part, high up, it is the other way round. This continues until the temperature differences have been eliminated. But if the heating in the one room is left on, we obtain, after a time, a closed stationary air flow system since the total amount of air in our room does not change.

A thermal circulation system is created in this way whenever there is differential heating, for instance, between land and sea, or mountains and plains, or a big city (in the extreme case, a big fire) and its surroundings, and between woods and fields. Differences in the intensity of incoming radiation during the day create local wind systems which change their direction when night falls. Differential heating during the day is usually more marked than at night, and the heat transmission T_L between ground and air at midday, when air layers are unstable, is much greater than at night when they are stable. For these reasons local winds are generally stronger during the day than at night and move in the reverse direction, since the temperature gradient is reversed. Of course these local wind systems can be superseded or suppressed by large and powerful currents dependent on the overall weather conditions. A general practice in meteorology is to name these local winds according to the direction from which they blow near the ground. So on the coast we have *sea breezes* during the day, and appreciably weaker *land breezes* at night. Under favourable conditions in the tropics, such a system can attain a horizontal dimension of 200–300 km, and a vertical development of 1–2 km. Above it, at heights of 3–4 km, the return current blows in the opposite direction, but it is usually much weaker. In mountain valleys, because of the differential heating of surfaces and the free air at different altitudes, we have upslope winds known as *valley breezes* during the day, and downslope winds known as *mountain breezes* at night. These nocturnal breezes are locally reinforced by the gravitational flow of layers of air cooled by contact with the ground, which form 'lakes' of cold air in the valleys.

If we postulate the existence of a non-rotating terrestrial globe which is heated strongly at the equator by solar radiation, and weakly at the two poles, except in winter when there would be no heating at all, we would expect a thermal circulation between the high and the low latitudes. Polar cold air would flow in low layers towards the equator, while tropical warm air would flow above towards the poles. If such a system remained stationary, the air masses would rise in the lower latitudes and sink in the polar latitudes. Since, however, the parallels of latitude become progressively smaller towards the poles, the upward movement of air would be restricted to the zone between 0° and 30° latitude, and the downward movement to the zone between 30° and 90° latitude, both areas being equal in size.

But our globe takes 24 hours to make a complete rotation about its axis, during which the velocity of rotation is 1,670 km/h at the equator, 1,180 km/h at a latitude of 45°, and 835 km/h at a latitude of 60°. The speed at which the earth rotates at a latitude of 57–60° is equal to the speed of modern jet aircraft so that an aircraft flying due west at that speed remains stationary in space while the earth's surface below it moves due east and the height of the sun remains unaltered. This enables passengers in commercial aircraft flying between Europe and America at the normal cruising height of 11 km above the tropopause to have a fascinating view of the unchanging oblique illumination of the clouds.

One of the basic laws of physics is that a body will continue to move in a straight line unless diverted from its path by another force. This applies not only to outer space, but also to the atmosphere, where the friction of the air molecules has only a small effect. However, although this law applies to space, it does not apply to our earthly system of co-ordinates since the earth itself rotates. Once this is grasped we realise that the earth and our system of co-ordinates will rotate away from a straight line

36 Sea breezes during the day (*top*) and land breezes during the night (*bottom*).

91

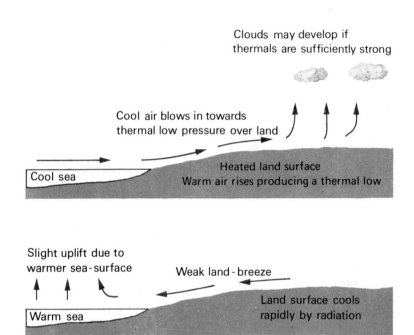

Clouds may develop if thermals are sufficiently strong

Cool air blows in towards thermal low pressure over land

Cool sea

Heated land surface
Warm air rises producing a thermal low

Slight uplift due to warmer sea-surface

Weak land-breeze

Warm sea

Land surface cools rapidly by radiation

followed by an unaccelerated body moving above it. But since we ourselves rotate with the earth it will appear to us that it is the body which is rotating.

Because of the force of attraction exerted by the mass of the earth (gravitation), there is a virtually constant gravitational force. The gravitational force holds the atmosphere to the earth and sets a limit to its upper boundary. If we face in the direction of air movement, its apparent rotation is in a clockwise direction in the Northern Hemisphere, and in an anti-clockwise direction in the Southern Hemisphere. At the equator there is no apparent rotation. Thus an air particle that has been set in motion but is not subjected to any other force than that of gravitation describes a circle of inertia round the earth. But as other forces are always involved, such a circle of inertia can be observed only intermittently over short distances.

If we retain our rotating system of co-ordinates, as fixed by all its earth-bound points, we can postulate the existence of an imaginary force which causes this apparent deflection. We speak therefore of a deflecting force due to the earth's rotation, known as the *Coriolis force*, which gives a lateral acceleration force with respect to our earth-bound system of co-ordinates, to moving air and indeed to all moving bodies on earth (Coriolis was a Greek mathematician who lived in Paris about 1830).

The rotation of the earth on its axis is demonstrated very clearly by the classic pendulum experiment made by Foucault in 1850. When a heavy weight is suspended from a high ceiling by a thin wire and is then set in motion and allowed to swing freely, the direction of the swing will apparently change in relation to our fixed frame of reference. In reality, however, it is our fixed frame of reference, that is, the earth, which continues to rotate beneath the pendulum. It rotates through 360° in 24 hours at the pole or through 360°/sine ϕ, where ϕ is the latitude. So from the point of view of an observer who is rotating with the earth, there is an apparent deflecting force in the virtually frictionless atmosphere with its earth-bound system of co-ordinates, north being in the direction of the geographical pole, with the east-west line invariably perpendicular to it.

The horizontal component of this apparent force 'C' depends on the velocity v of the moving particle, the earth's angular velocity ω, and the geographical latitude ϕ.

$$C = 2 \, \omega \, \text{sine} \, \phi \times v.$$

If we hold a transparent sheet of paper on which we have drawn a meridional line above a globe and then rotate the globe, we immediately see that the maximum apparent deflection of the meridian occurs at the poles, and that at the equator it is zero. We

37 The Coriolis force. If we consider a particle of air moving horizontally away from the North Pole (**P**) at a velocity v in the direction of point **A**, which it should reach in time t, it will soon become affected by the earth's rotation ω. Since the earth's surface is rotating with counter-clockwise angular velocity ω, the point **A** will have moved to **B** in the time t, and **A′** moved to **A**. Thus, relative to the earth's surface, the particle will appear to have followed the path **PA′**, or to have undergone a continuous deflection of its movement to the right.

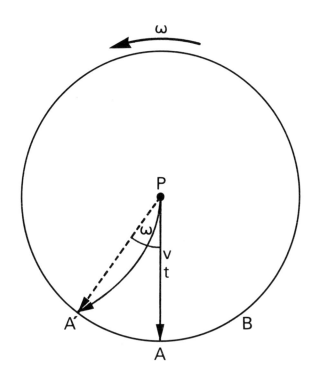

94

38 Vector diagram to show the
balanced wind flow in the
Northern Hemisphere. **a** includes
the pressure gradient force and
geostrophic force only. **b** shows
the additional effect of friction.
39 The differential reduction in pressure
with altitude in cold (**C**) air and
warm (**W**) air in the transition
area and frontal zone.

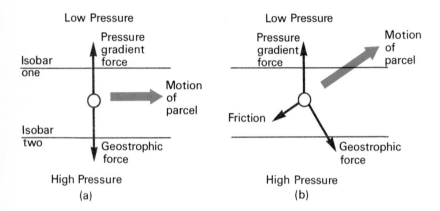

(a)   (b)

also see that the deflection at one pole is in the opposite direction to
that at the other.

Before we return to the question of thermal circulation between
two differentially heated zones, we must consider the subject of air
pressure again so that we have a thorough understanding of what
is involved. Air pressure decreases with height, since the air above
us becomes progressively rarer. The colder, and therefore heavier,
the atmosphere is, the faster is the upward decrease in pressure.
The warmer, and therefore lighter, the atmosphere is, the slower is
the upward decrease in pressure.

If, therefore, a cold and warm air mass lie side by side at the same
ground pressure, we have a pressure gradient with a slope rising
from the warm air towards the cold air. This, in fact, is a basic law
in aerology. At a high altitude pressure is high in the warm air

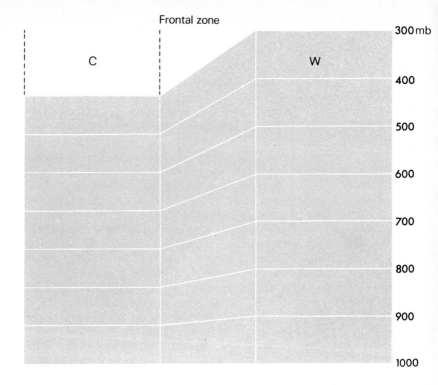

Frontal zone

C

W

300 mb
400
500
600
700
800
900
1000

(200 mb near the tropopause) and low in the cold air. Between the warm and the cold air there is a zone in which there is a steep temperature gradient corresponding to a pressure gradient increasing upward. This transition zone is known as a *frontal zone*.

If the earth were not rotating, such a pressure gradient would cause the upper air to move towards an area of lower pressure, that is, towards the cold air. To compensate for this, the cold air near the ground, in which the pressure rises in response to this air movement above, will then move towards the warm air. Our model of the thermal circulation between warm air and cold air is therefore coupled with a pressure gradient which changes its direction of slope with height.

Such thermal air movements arise all over the world as a result of the differences in the radiation and heat balances and are concurrently associated with pressure differences in various parts of the atmosphere; for as soon as there is a pressure gradient, air moves from areas of high pressure towards areas of low pressure. But when such movements occur on a rather larger scale, over distances of, say, 10 km, and a period of, say, an hour, we can no longer ignore the ever-present deflecting force caused by the earth's rotation. This is always perpendicular to the direction of movement of the air. If the movement is to be brought into equilibrium, then the deflecting force of the rotation of the earth C must necessarily be equal and opposite to the force of the pressure gradient G. In the free atmosphere this usually happens above the lower 1,000–1,500 metres or ground friction layer and the wind then blows perpendicularly to the pressure gradient, or in different terms, parallel to the isobars (lines of constant pressure). When there is such a stable equilibrium, we speak of the *geostrophic wind*, from the Greek 'strophein', meaning 'revolving', and 'geo', meaning 'earth'. If we face the direction in which the wind is blowing, then in the Northern Hemisphere the pressure is lower on our left-hand side and in the Southern Hemisphere, on the right-hand side.

Near the ground another force is added, the force of friction with the surface of the earth, R, which brakes the movement of air. If equilibrium is to be obtained, then the pressure gradient force must be equal to the resultant of the surface friction force and the Coriolis force. Because of surface friction, the wind always blows at an angle towards the lower pressure. The angle between the ground surface wind (measured at a height of 10 metres according to international convention) and the isobars, depends on the roughness of the ground surface. On an average this angle is less than 10° above the sea, and 30°–40° above land.

The wind increases with height and becomes gradually almost parallel to the isobars. At a height of a 1,000 metres the difference between the geostrophic wind calculated from the pressure gradient and the figures obtained by direct measurement is very small.

The following forces therefore act on an air particle moving in a linear pressure field.

1 Gravitation, which affects only the vertical component of the wind.

2 The vertical pressure gradient force from high pressure near the earth to low pressure at higher levels; for practical considerations this is balanced by gravitation.

3 The horizontal pressure gradient force G.

4 The deflective force of the earth's rotation C.

5 The surface friction R, along the ground which, however, can be discounted at heights above 1,000 metres.

When the isobars are curved, that is, when there are *centres* of high and low pressure, the winds follow a curved path, and another force, the *centrifugal force*, also operates on the moving air particle. This is a force directed outward from the centre of rotation, and its size is proportional to the square of the velocity and inversely proportional to the radius of curvature. It plays an important role, therefore, in tropical storms with their high windspeeds and small radii of curvature, but in the larger anticyclones it is of only small consequence.

When all these forces are in equilibrium, the air particle remains stationary. However, as soon as the equilibrium is disturbed, the movement of the air particle is accelerated in one direction or another or held back or deflected. A stationary equilibrium never actually occurs because the wind is never constant and is always subject to variations in velocity and direction. If the earth were a homogeneous billiard ball and the radiation balance depended only on the height of the sun, and if the transmission of heat from ground to air and the roughness of the ground surface were uniform, we could expect almost stationary (quasi-stationary) conditions. But recent laboratory experiments and calculations with computers have shown that even under these conditions, there would still always be some waves and vortices.

To understand the vast circulation system of the atmosphere we have first to consider the temperature distribution between the troposphere and the lower stratosphere resulting from the radiation balance. In the tropical zone where there is a large net surplus of radiation energy, temperatures are very high (25°–27°C near the ground). Between latitudes 30° and 65°, the temperature decreases rapidly towards the poles, whereas at the polar caps, at latitudes beyond 65°, temperatures are nearly always low. Thus in both hemispheres there is a transition zone between the tropical and subtropical warm air and the polar cold air, which we can call a *planetary frontal zone*. This is a zone in which there are strong west winds which increase with height up to 200 mb (about 12 km). This zone is the region of the *mid-latitude westerlies*.

Waves and *vortices* constantly form in this zone as the result of differential heating and also of physical deflection by high mountain ranges and plateaux. For a long time these waves and vortices were regarded as an almost incidental disturbance of a hypothetical mean state. Yet together they are the essential elements of the general circulation of the atmosphere. In the upper troposphere and the lower stratosphere, that is, at altitudes between 4–16 km, huge, long-waves predominate. These gigantic meandering waves have a width and length of 3,000–6,000 km and remain almost stationary or move rather slowly, mostly from west to east, and always in a state of fluctuation. They are formed, in part at least, by the great mountain ranges of this earth, that is the Western Cordillera of North America, the mountain chains and plateaux of central Asia, and in the Southern Hemisphere, the Andes of South America, and the South Africa Plateau.

In the lower troposphere, on the other hand, vortices with diameters of 1,000–2,000 km predominate, rotating in a clockwise and anti-clockwise direction. We will discuss these vortices – the cyclones (low pressure areas), and anticyclones (high pressure areas) – in chapter 4. The vortices are the near-surface equivalents of travelling waves with shorter wavelengths in the currents above, but as the structure of such whorls is asymmetric, warm air in a vortex invariably flows towards the poles, while cold air flows towards the equator. Since at the same time the deflecting force of

40 Vertical temperature distribution
at the equator (**E**), the South Pole (**S**) and
the North Pole (**N**) for January and July.
The circles are the mean maximum monthly
temperatures (July) over southern Asia.

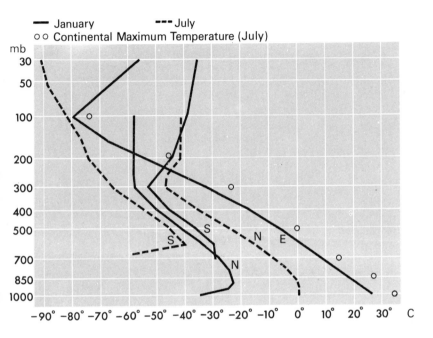

— January   --- July
○○ Continental Maximum Temperature (July)

the earth's rotation increases in the direction of the poles, the vortices are forced out of the zone of the westerlies by a weak but statistically significant shear force component.

Cyclones usually travel with one component directed polewards, which causes the formation of a zone of cyclonic whorls at a latitude of between 55°–65°, which is known as the *subpolar low pressure zone*. On the other hand, anticyclones travel with one component directed towards the equator, where they unite with the high pressure zones which are common in that region to form the cells of the *subtropical high pressure belt* at latitudes of 30°–40°. In this way the cells are constantly regenerated. Both processes and their numerous modifications can be followed on any series of weather charts covering a whole hemisphere.

In the subtropics and tropics these subtropical anticyclones form a pressure gradient which slopes towards the equator and forms in consequence, a gradient wind from the east – the widespread tropical easterly flow which, however, is appreciably weaker than the extratropical westerlies. This flow usually decreases with heights, at least over the great oceans, and at heights of 10–12 km it is commonly overlapped by westerly winds.

Close to the ground these regular easterly winds, known as *trade winds*, blow with a weak component directed towards the low pressure area near the equator. The trade winds from east-north-east in the Northern Hemisphere and from east-south-east in the Southern Hemisphere, meet at a sharp angle in the *equatorial trough* of *low pressure*. The meeting of winds from different directions is known as a convergence; the reverse process as a divergence. The equatorial trough of low pressure, viewed globally, if not locally, corresponds to an *intertropical convergence zone*. This term is frequently used in its abbreviated form as I.T.C. or I.T.C.Z.

If the winds converge near the ground, the air must rise since it cannot take any sideways or downward avoiding action. Cooling therefore sets in, and as soon as the temperature is below the dew-point, clouds form, followed later by precipitation. This is the reason why areas of low pressure and convergence zones are usually characterised by thick cloud and precipitation.

If the surface winds diverge in anticyclonic cells, cold air sinks to compensate and in doing so becomes warmer. The result is that clouds dissipate and the weather becomes predominantly fine. This shows us at once the reason for the difference between the predominantly dry and fine weather in subtropical high pressure regions, and the wet and cloudy tropical convergence zone near the equator.

The meridional circulation in low latitudes is therefore as follows. Close to the ground, a component blows towards the equator at an average velocity of 1–2 m/s or 4–7 km/h. In the intertropical convergence zone air rises at an average velocity of only 1–2 cm/s at a maximum. Higher up, near the 200 mb level, this rising air diverges towards the poles at a speed of up to 2 m/s. A slight descending component in velocity by a few mm/s occurs predominantly in the zone of subtropical high pressure cells.

This tropical circulation closely resembles the thermal circulation we discussed with reference to a stationary globe. The cool low-level trade winds blow towards the equator, while at a higher level the wind blows towards the poles. But the earth's rotation subordinates this circulation to the global system of winds blowing more or less parallel to the latitudes. The average velocity of the tropical easterly winds is 6–10 m/s while the velocity of the westerlies in the subtropical zone at a height of nearly 12 km, where the highest speeds are reached, is about 30 m/s (108 km/h). These winds are therefore stronger than the middle meridional-vertical trade winds by one or several orders of magnitude.

The wind component directed to the poles at heights of 10–12 km is known as an *anti-trade wind*. But it is formed partly by the offshoots of the extratropical westerly winds, and partly by temporarily stationary meander oscillations, in which the north and south components continually interchange. Only averaged over an entire zone of latitude do these components towards the poles normally outweigh the effect of the opposite components.

In the upper troposphere, it is the meandering waves of the westerly winds that play the dominant role and frequently influence the weather conditions in the lower troposphere. Closer examination shows that the weather in the tropics is as varied and changeable as it is in the middle and higher latitudes. It is only along the coastlines and in mountainous regions that diurnal wind systems prevail and give a visitor the impression of regular weather conditions.

Close to the ground the trade winds themselves are deflected slightly towards the equator by friction. The result of this component directed towards the equator is a slight divergence in

41 *Below* Upper air of the jet stream. The diagram shows a sequence of disturbances (called the Index Cycle) in these upper-air waves. The amplitude of the waves increases until they both become unstable and break, leaving pools of cool air (blue) in low latitudes, with warmer air (grey) at higher latitudes. These cut-off features give rise to unusual weather in the respective latitudes.

42 *Right* Mean zonal winds over the earth in summer and winter. Isotachs (lines of equal wind speed) are in metres per second. Regions of easterly winds are blue. The reversal from surface easterlies to upper westerlies shows clearly between latitudes 15° and 30°.

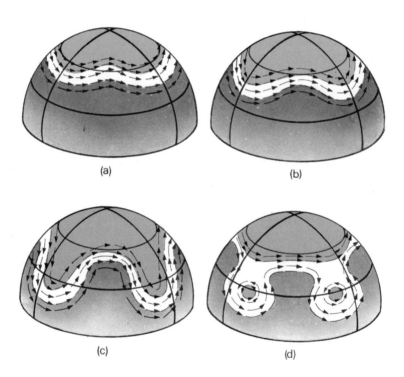

(a)

(b)

(c)

(d)

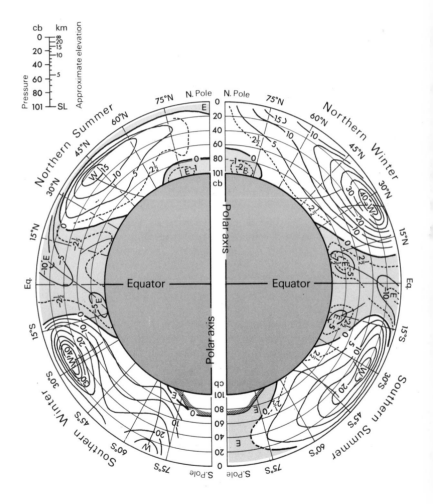

relation to the rotating earth and a consequent subsidence of air with the formation of a strong and stable trade wind inversion at an altitude of 1,000–2,000 m. This separates the moist, unstable lower base layer of the trade wind airstream which carries billowing clouds, from an upper layer which is practically cloud-free.

The base layer of the trade wind airstream constantly receives latent heat (T_V) from the evaporating water and also a small quantity of sensible heat (T_L) from the somewhat warmer surface of the sea. These processes of evaporation and heating play a very important role in the general circulation and in the heat and water budget of the atmosphere.

In polar regions, the irregular movements of the whorls of cyclones and anticyclones originating in the westerly wind zone in middle latitudes determine the course of the weather. A slight poleward increase in pressure with an insignificant preponderance of easterly winds in the lower layers is encountered beyond the subpolar trough of low pressure, but only as a statistical average over an entire latitudinal zone. Above lie the tropospheric cold poles of the Arctic and the Antarctic, which are often asymmetrically displaced from the geographic poles and form the centre of the gigantic polar whorls of the encircling extratropical westerly winds. In the Northern Hemisphere winter the snow-covered northern regions of the great Asian and North American continents are always colder, even in the middle and upper troposphere, than the inner Arctic regions, where there is always a strong heat flow from the ocean into the atmosphere through the ice cover, which is only 150–250 cm thick. In this period, from November to March, the Arctic polar whorl splits into two cells which normally lie above the central part of the Canadian archipelago and above eastern Siberia. In spring, that is in the months of April and May, vast stationary high pressure zones lasting for several weeks often form in the Arctic in conjunction with a warm troposphere. This, however, is rare in other seasons. The cold centre, or 'cold pole', may then be displaced to beyond the Arctic circle. This also happens during severe winters in the northern continents. The cold poles sometimes move down to a latitude of 50°, taking up some heat in the process. Sometimes they even reach the subtropics, albeit in a weakened form, as 'cold air pools'.

On the edge of the great inland ice region in Greenland and in the Antarctic, very strong *katabatic winds* flow from the ice towards the sea, which is always warmer because of the laws governing local thermal circulation. Before aerological observations were made regularly, these winds led to the mistaken belief that there was a high pressure region above the ice shield. But for all their intensity and regularity, these winds blow in an atmospheric layer which is only 100–300 metres deep, while the migrating 'perturbations' pass above unhindered over the ice caps which they feed with snow.

If we draw an idealised meridian cross-cut of the distribution of surface air pressure and the distribution of the great zonal wind systems, we obtain a purposely simplified diagram which is shown in table 4.

We have seen that in the tropics a much weaker meridional circulation system is superimposed on a system of zonal winds, and that it conveys relatively cooler air near the ground towards the equator and corresponding amounts of air higher up in the opposite direction. Owing to the deflecting power of the earth's rotation, however, this poleward-directed wind component increases the strength of the upper westerly wind over the sub-tropical high pressure cells, which is where, on the average, they attain their greatest velocities. We are referring here to a *sub-tropical jet stream*, which is not, however, stationary. The essential properties of the basic jet streams are discussed in more detail in chapter 4.

The general circulation of the air within the atmosphere provides the varied and vast air transfers which are maintaining the present patterns of our climate. It transports warmer air from the tropical and subtropical latitudes towards the poles and colder air towards the equator. In 1920 the Yugoslav astronomer Milankovitch

Table 4

Hemisphere		Air pressure belt	Wind systems	Upper boundary
South	North			
90°	90°	Polar high		
			Polar east winds	2–3 km
65°	65°–75°	Subpolar low pressure trough		
			Extra-tropical westerly winds	Summer: 18–22 km Winter: 80 km
25°–30°	30°–40°	Subtropical high pressure trough		
			Tropical easterly winds	Ocean 6–10 km Continent (at least above 20 km)
	0–10°N	Equatorial low pressure trough		

calculated, from certain basic assumptions, with the help of a model, that if the atmosphere were stationary, the average temperature in the inner tropics would be 32–33°C, instead of 26–27°C, and −40°C at the North Pole instead of about −17°C. This levelling off of temperature by the transfer of sensible heat is one of the most important results of the circulation of the atmosphere, which, conversely, is kept in motion by the interplay of heating and cooling. The circulation also maintains a moisture balance by transporting water-vapour and its latent heat from zones where evaporation is predominant to zones where precipitation is predominant and also between the oceans, which provide almost 90% of the water-vapour in the atmosphere, and the continents. It is also relevant to another transfer process whose importance is generally less well known outside specialist circles. This is the transfer of angular momentum. Since the direction of the rotation of the earth is from west to east, all easterly winds have a braking effect on the earth's surface, whereas all westerly winds have an accelerating effect. But the law of conservation of angular momentum requires that the sum of the angular momentum in the system 'earth + atmosphere' remains constant. In the easterly wind regions surface friction does indeed transfer westerly angular momentum from the earth to the atmosphere, whereas in westerly wind regions, the opposite occurs, and the more rapidly rotating atmosphere transfers angular momentum to the earth. This is possible only when the atmosphere transfers angular momentum from the tropics and also to a much smaller extent from the polar caps to the middle latitudes.

The sum of these transfers maintains the heat and water balances and the rotation of the system 'earth + atmosphere + hydrosphere (oceans)'. For the surface currents of the oceans, whose movements play a decisive role in the heat and water balances, are predominantly wind driven.

All transfers are effected by a number of different but interconnected mechanisms, of which the transfer by means of the mean meridional circulation in tropical latitudes is only one of them. In this case the transfer takes the form of horizontal spirals, the lower branches being directed to the equator, the higher ones to the poles. In the middle and upper troposphere, however, this type of transfer is of minor importance compared with another type, the horizontal exchange by means of adjacent lying cells, with a partly northerly and partly southerly component. This type of exchange is effected in an irregular manner by the travelling vortices and meandering waves of the great westerly winds. Waves and vortices which remain stationary or almost stationary (quasi-stationary) at one point have the same effect. Two forms of transfer intermingle in the subtropics: the mean meridional circulation in the tropics which originates mainly in the lower troposphere, and the irregular horizontal exchange in the middle and higher latitudes which extends into higher layers.

In specialised literature the first form is often referred to as the Hadley or meridional type, the latter as the Ferrel or eddy type of circulation, following the classic work of G. Hadley in 1735, and W. Ferrel in 1855. Recent laboratory investigations carried out by D. Fultz of Chicago, have shown that the relationship between these two types depends on a few single physical values. These include the rotational velocity of the earth and the meridional temperature gradient (and so the strength of the westerly winds).

It is worth noting that there is also a very weak meridional circulation within the extratropical westerly wind zone. It is much weaker and even more irregular than the tropical circulation. This type of circulation, in which warm air flows below towards the pole and cold air flows above towards the equator, runs in the opposite direction from the thermal circulation and has to be maintained by ground surface friction. While the 'direct' Hadley circulation of the tropical cell produces mechanical work from heat energy the 'indirect' circulation in the region of the westerlies, with cold air rising and warm air sinking, requires mechanical work to maintain it. The still weaker and more irregular polar cell of the meridional circulation is again 'direct' but quantitatively insignificant.

In this age of space research it is obviously of interest to compare the circulation of the earth's atmosphere with that of other planets and the sun. To do this, as we already know, we need consider only a few basic parameters. The angular momentum of the earth (radius r) is $r\omega$ at the equator and $r\omega \cos \phi$ at latitude ϕ. The 'thermal' wind U^*, produced by the meridional temperature gradient at the upper boundary of the layer under consideration, can be represented as a 'thermal Rossby number' Ro_T, which gives the relationship between U^* and $r\omega$, while the kinematic Rossby number gives the relationship between the actual zonal wind U and the equatorial velocity of the surface. The thermal Rossby number is very small in the tropics. The Hadley system, with its horizontal spiralling movements lying one above the other, related symmetrically to the earth's axis, is predominant here. As U^* increases with the latitude, so does the thermal Rossby number. In the upper troposphere, the irregular Ferrel type of exchange between adjacent cells, no longer related symmetrically to the earth's axis, is increasingly prevalent. The occurrence of both types of circulation is therefore a function of two planetarian properties of the earth's atmosphere. These are the equatorial rotational velocity $r\omega$ as well as the thermal wind U^*, or the mean temperature gradient between the equator and pole.

The lower temperatures in the Antarctic troposphere result in higher values of U^* in the Southern Hemisphere, that is, the Ferrel circulation spreads out close to and even beyond the equator. This relationship, which can be expressed in figures by making certain simplifications, becomes more important when we deal with the problems of the climate of the geological past, and particularly when we are considering the artificial modification of climate on a world-wide scale.

In our review of the general atmospheric circulation as a whole, we have not fully taken into account the different influences of land and sea, and of summer and winter. These, however, are very important in regional climates. We must start with the assumption that the seasonal variation of the zenithal position and the maximum radiation of the sun from 23°S in December to 23°N in June necessarily results in a meridional displacement of the air pressure and wind belts shown in table 4. Next, we will notice in table 4 that the equatorial trough of low pressure on a planetary average always occurs between latitude 0–10° in the Northern Hemisphere. Seasonal displacements are particularly pronounced over the two oceans, the Pacific and the Atlantic, which stretch from pole to pole. In winter in the Northern Hemisphere (January), we find the intertropical convergence, with temporary exceptions, at the equator itself. On the other hand, in summer (July) we find it at a latitude of 10–12°N. There is no doubt that the asymmetrical distribution of land and sea has an effect here, as the large continents cause intense heating of the Northern Hemisphere during the summer (June–August). For the same reason there is strong cooling in winter but the I.T.C. above the ocean still remains north of the equator. The predominant cause becomes clear if we remember that the troposphere above the ice-covered Antarctic continent is always 10–12°C colder than above the Arctic Ocean with its thin layer of ice. This difference of temperature is obviously caused by a markedly different heat balance, especially in the summer when almost 90% of the incoming solar radiation above the Antarctic is immediately reflected, while a relatively large amount of energy is available to heat the air above the Arctic. In winter heat passes into the atmosphere from the water of the Arctic Ocean with temperatures of about 1–2°C through the heat-conducting ice layer, while the air has a temperature of about −35°C or below. Intensive cooling from below of the Antarctic air results in temperatures down to −70°C, and in extreme cases, even to −88°C. An additional factor is probably that the horizontal heat exchange in the middle and higher latitudes is greater in the Northern Hemisphere than in the Southern Hemisphere which is almost completely covered by water.

Since the temperature of the intertropical heat reservoir is the same for both hemispheres, the temperature gradient from the equator to the pole, which determines the intensity of the westerlies and the general circulation, is nearly 40% greater over the Southern Hemisphere than over the Northern Hemisphere. The stronger circulation in the Southern Hemisphere therefore spreads towards the equator. The centre of the subtropical high pressure belt in the Southern Hemisphere lies on average over 30°S, that is 7° latitude nearer the equator than in the Northern Hemisphere (37°N), and the tropical Hadley cell extends across the equator into the Northern Hemisphere. This explains the characteristic asymmetric arrangement of the intertropical convergence zone which is rightly described as a 'meteorological equator'.

The seasonal displacement of the air pressure and wind belts depends mainly on the direct heating of the air by the factor T_L in the heat balance. But this factor is five to seven times greater over the tropical and subtropical continents than over the tropical oceans where evaporation uses up practically all the available energy. The amounts, according to Budyko, are 96 Ly/day over land in the zone 30°N to 30°S as compared with 16 Ly/day over the oceans. For this reason the seasonal displacements of the system are much greater over the continents than over the oceans. This is clearly demonstrated by a direct comparison between the situation in Africa on the one hand and the Pacific on the other. Over Africa the intertropical convergence shifts from about 18°S in January to 18°N in July whereas over the Pacific it always stays in a belt between 0° and 10°N. Many valuable observations have been made of the weather along the main sea routes between Europe and South America, even though in summer the section along the African coast is not strictly oceanic in character. The intertropical convergence in the Atlantic reaches 11°N in August and 1°N from February to March. Over south Asia, in the north-western regions of the Indian subcontinent, the I.T.C. shifts in July and August to as far as 30°N, and over north Australia in January and February, to about 21°S.

From this we can postulate, both on a theoretical and an empirical basis that on a homogeneous globe whose surface was all land, the intertropical convergence zone would follow the

43 Mean positions of the intertropical convergence zone in January and July.

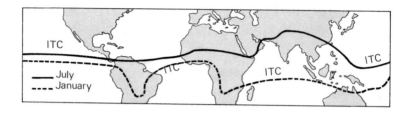

zenithal sun with a lag of about 1 month, and almost reach both tropics (23° latitude). On the other hand, on a globe whose surface was entirely water, with the heat balance components symmetrically distributed, we would expect fluctuations to occur on both sides of the equator to a maximum amount of ±5° latitude. This fundamental difference results from the different reactions of land and sea to insolation, that is, the different behaviour of the factors T_M and T_L in the heat budget.

In the *oceanic regions*, with a few exceptions, the lower layers of the trade winds in both hemispheres meet directly in the I.T.C. In the same way, offshoots of the westerly winds frequently reach the equator from both sides at an altitude of 10–12 km, and come into contact with one another, or else they are interconnected by a chain of cyclonic or anticyclonic vortices. Such a wind distribution can exist only when the highest mean values of pressure and temperature in the upper troposphere are recorded in the immediate neighbourhood of the equator and there is a continuous fall of both pressure and temperature from the inner tropics towards polar regions.

Over the *continents*, we find that the highest temperatures are recorded in both winter and summer in the neighbourhood of the tropics where the sun is at its highest zenith and insolation is at a maximum. Shallow thermal depressions in the northern summer stretch like a chain from the Sahara, across Arabia and Iraq, or over south Iran, to the Punjab; they are also found in Arizona in the south-west of the North American continent. The resultant pressure gradient sloping poleward from the mathematical equator leads to the development of a shallow equatorial westerly flow, deflected on the ground towards the S.W. by ground surface friction, which we can follow in July and August from the west coast of Africa over India, and right across to beyond the Philippines. On the other hand, in the middle and upper troposphere in winter and summer, the pressure gradient slopes towards the equator, accompanied by an easterly flow reaching into the stratosphere which always separates the extratropical westerlies of both hemispheres. Even between seasons there is often an easterly wind zone extending to great altitudes with some shallow westerly winds embedded in it. As a consequence of this wind pattern, the intertropical convergence zone in these continental regions almost invariably splits into two branches; a primary branch in the region of the heat lows in the outer tropics, and a secondary, less obvious, branch in the neighbourhood of the equator. Figure 44 shows two meridional cross-sections of the zonal winds in schematic form – one over an ocean section and the other over a continental section.

The air pressures and wind belts in higher latitude continental areas also shift according to the seasons. This applies particularly to the subtropical high pressure zone which lies about 5–10° nearer the pole in summer than in winter. For this reason, in the cold season of the year, the extratropical west wind zone widens into the subtropics, an event which is much weaker at the oceans. But since both of the large northern continents, Asia and North America, are bounded in the direction of the poles by the Arctic Ocean, the subpolar low pressure trough displaces itself in the reverse direction. In winter it lies above the relatively warmer polar seas, and in the summer over the strongly heated inner regions of the continents. These seasonal shifts also lead to a seasonal change of nearly 180° in the direction of the prevailing wind in many continental regions. We can describe the seasonal change in the direction of the winds as a 'monsoon'. This term has, in fact, nothing to do with the course of the weather conditions over the year, nor with the temperature differences between land

and sea. We will revert to it in chapter 5. The word 'mausim', monsoon, has been used by Arab seamen for over a thousand years to describe the seasonal change in wind direction – north-easterly in the cold season, south-westerly in the hot season – in the sea regions between Arabia and India. They have used this knowledge to plan their journeys across the seas.

There are three continental zones in which there is a marked annual change of wind direction, although this may not always apply to all areas in these zones. These three zones are:
1 Near the subpolar low pressure trough where polar easterly winds blow in the summer and westerly winds in the winter.
2 Near the subtropical high pressure cells where westerly winds blow in the winter and easterly trade winds (calms) in the summer.
3 Near the intertropical convergence zone where easterly trade winds blow in the winter and westerly winds in the summer.

The first of these zones, the zone of the polar monsoons, owes its existence to the pattern of distribution of land and sea in the subarctic. In the Southern Hemisphere the pattern is reversed, and because of this and the ice (with its high albedo) which covers the Antarctic continent, it does not have a corresponding effect on the wind and air pressure belt. The second and third zones would also exist over a homogeneous land-covered globe because of the seasonal shift in the direction of solar radiation, but they would be absent from a globe in which the whole surface was covered with water.

There is a seasonal change of wind direction, which can also be called a monsoon, in the stratosphere and the mesosphere. The latitudinal absorption of the sun's radiation, including that reflected from clouds and the surface of the earth, usually results in a continuous temperature gradient from the warm summer pole, across the equator, to the cold winter pole. This uniform tempera-ture and pressure gradient, however, corresponds with a wind direction which in one hemisphere is opposite to that in the other. For the same reason we can observe the regular occurrence of

44 Idealised meridional cross-section of the distribution of east (**E**) and west (**W**) winds over an oceanic (Pacific) and a continental (African) sector. Double lines = tropopause and **J** = jet stream (**P** = polar front, **S** = subtropical, **PN** = polar night). J_T = tropical easterly jet stream, J_K = Krakatoa easterly air stream, W_B = Berson westerly air stream. The latter two vary in position periodically.

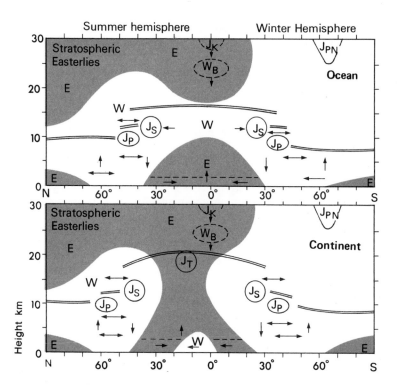

easterly winds above 18–20 km in the summer hemisphere, and westerly winds in the winter hemisphere. Both systems extend upward to a height of about 80 km.

During the polar winter the sun disappears completely within a shadow cone up to 500 km high centred on the pole. Since no solar radiation is then absorbed, this results in considerable cooling. Around this stratospheric cold pole, at a height of 20–35 km, there is a zone with a very steep temperature gradient and correspondingly very strong westerly winds – the so-called *polar night jet stream*. The various anomalies associated with this jet stream have in recent years become the subject of particular interest to meteorologists. Unfortunately we are not able to discuss the details here.

The atmospheric circulation on our globe is influenced not only by the disposition of the land and sea masses, but also by high mountain ranges and highlands in general. For dynamic reasons alone the great wind systems tend to deviate in an anticyclonic sense as they cross mountain ranges and high land. This tendency is further strengthened by the fact that high-lying heated surfaces, provided they are not completely covered with snow and ice, heat the air layers above them more strongly than low-level surface heating would heat the air at a comparable level. Similarly the formation of clouds and precipitation in areas where the prevailing winds are forced upwards causes the release of considerable amounts of latent heat of condensation. A precipitation of 10 mm/day, or 1 gram/cm^2 liberates almost twice as much energy (600 Ly/day) as the radiation balance over land under favourable circumstances.

The anticyclonic deflection of the great wind systems brought about by dynamic and thermal means is transmitted upwards into the layer of maximum wind velocities which lies 10–12 km high. This, again, for dynamic reasons which were expressed by C. J. Rossby in 1940 in a simplified mathematical form, leads to the development of a second but this time cyclonic deflection in the opposite direction at a distance of about 1,500–2,000 km from the first. In these regions, to the lee of high mountain ranges such as the Western Cordillera of North America or the highlands of central Asia, meandering oscillations of the westerlies constantly develop anew and travel eastward. On average, a nearly stationary (quasi-stationary) low pressure trough forms between these two systems, which usually reaches deep into the subtropics and displaces the subtropic high pressure cells sideways. The extra-tropical westerlies and the tropical circulation may interact in these sectors and cyclonic disturbances from both sides may cause perturbations in a meridional direction.

This occurs mainly in the following regions (E = east):

NORTHERN HEMISPHERE:

East and central North America	= 75°–85° longitude W
East Asia	= 110°–120° longitude E

SOUTHERN HEMISPHERE:

East coast of South America	= 40°–50° W, which is a little uncertain
East coast of South Africa	= 40°–50° E
Region of New Zealand	= 170°–180°E

Weaker troughs, classed as secondary meander oscillations, also occur, particularly in winter and spring in the Northern Hemisphere; they are found at 20°–30°E in eastern Europe, and in summer at 140°W off the west coast of North America, as well as at 100°E off the west coast of Australia in the Southern Hemisphere.

4 Weather and weather forecasting

4 Weather and weather forecasting

In considering the general circulation of the atmosphere we have already discussed a series of factors which play a major part in creating weather conditions. The daily course of the weather with all its variations is an inexhaustible subject of conversation in the middle and upper latitudes and particularly in Europe. But the careful observer who watches weather changes from the same spot never sees more than a small section of it, even if he is in a mountain weather station with an unimpeded view of cloud and sky.

To obtain a true picture of the seemingly random sequence of diverse weather conditions, it is necessary to record on one chart the observations made simultaneously at many points. This was done for the first time by Professor Brandes, a professor at the University of Leipzig, in 1817. He based his work on the observations made over many decades by the first international network of weather stations, that of the Meteorological Society of the Palatinate in Mannheim (1781–95). We call the recording of simultaneous meteorological phenomena 'synoptic meteorology', although 'synchronous meteorology' would perhaps be more appropriate.

The invention of the telegraph and all the means of communication based on it, such as radio and teleprinters, has made it possible for synoptic meteorology to cover vast areas and nowadays even the entire globe. The first readings, however, were made exclusively from ground stations. But since 1935 more and more use has been made of radio-sondes, which are aerological instruments suspended from a balloon. They measure the temperature, pressure, and moisture content of the air at heights up to 20–30 km. The results are transmitted by radio to a weather station and immediately recorded on maps. Today, as a result of international agreements, about 600 radio-sonde stations record such information every 12 hours, and often every 6 hours so far as the winds in the upper air are concerned. Similar measurements are made by 10,000 ground weather stations every 3 or 6 hours, and every 30 minutes at big airports.

Today it is possible for a central weather station to make a chart covering a whole hemisphere within 3 hours of receiving all the relevant information. Six hours later, a whole series of hemispherical weather charts are available, representing the conditions in various layers of the atmosphere at heights up to about 30 km, corresponding to a pressure of about 10 mb. Such weather maps are prepared anew every 6, 12, or 24 hours, and they are the basic working material of our meteorological services. They are also the basis of the weather forecasts which are transmitted all over the world by radio, telegraph and television.

But what do we actually see on these weather maps or charts? If we join together all the points with equal atmospheric pressure (isobars) on a ground weather chart we see at once that the wind, when not subject to local disturbances, more or less follows these isobars. The isobars enclose areas of high pressure (Highs) and areas of low pressure (Lows). We have already seen that near the ground winds are deflected towards low pressure.

For this reason, winds near the ground in a low pressure area (cyclones) blow with one component directed towards the centre of low pressure, while in high pressure areas (anticyclones) the near-surface winds blow with one component directed away from the centre of high pressure. Above this surface friction layer in the Northern Hemisphere, the winds circulate in an anti-clockwise direction in a low pressure area and in a clockwise direction in a high pressure area. In the Southern Hemisphere the opposite applies. The diameter of these systems is about 500–4,000 km. Several anticyclones and depressions can always be seen on any weather chart. Close to the ground, however, this pattern can be disturbed by the effect of mountain ranges, coastlines, and so on. From all this we see that in the lower air layers up to a height of about 3 km, there are two types of whorl, spinning in opposite directions.

If we look at the weather charts obtained at intervals of 3–6 hours, we see how the various pressure systems not only shift, but also grow or decrease in size, or merge into one another. We also see how all these changes are related to the course of the weather at

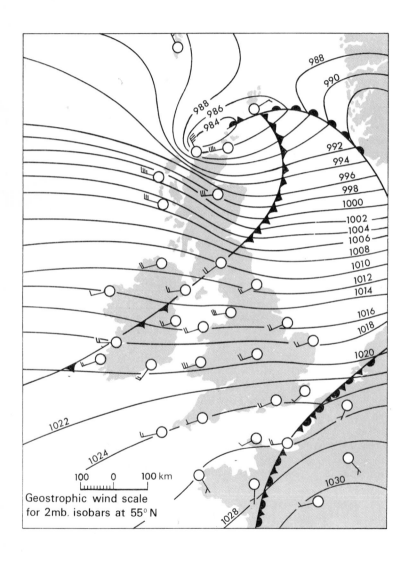

988
990
988
986
984
992
994
996
998
1000
1002
1004
1006
1008
1010
1012
1014
1016
1018
1020
1022
1024
1030
1028

100   0   100 km

Geostrophic wind scale
for 2mb. isobars at 55° N

45 and **46** Winds in the Northern Hemisphere (*left*)
and in the Southern Hemisphere (*below*).
Over the sea, winds are parallel to the isobars,
but over the land, frictional effects increase
and winds blow more across the isobars.

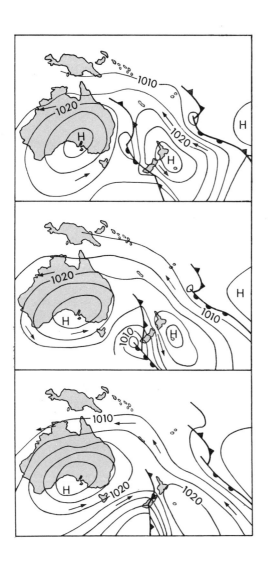

00 Hrs. G.M.T.
25 May 1941

00 Hrs. G.M.T.
26 May 1941

00 Hrs. G.M.T.
27 May 1941

any particular place. If we plot information on clouds and precipitation on our weather chart, then we see at once that extensive areas of fine weather are most frequently associated with the high pressure areas, whereas in the low pressure areas there are extensive zones of thick cloud and widespread precipitation. This is of course a generalisation which is not necessarily applicable to any particular situation. There is a simple explanation.

Ground winds in a high pressure area are divergent and air must sink from greater heights to compensate. In doing this it is heated adiabatically at the rate of 10°C/km, and so dissipates cloud. On the other hand, in a low pressure area, if the surface winds are convergent they are forced to ascend. This causes cooling which, when the temperature falls below the dew-point, results in the formation of clouds and precipitation.

The relationship between the slow upward and downward movements of the air and the course of the weather was first recognised by J. Hann in about 1865. The effect is particularly well illustrated when large masses of air cross mountain ranges: thick clouds form (liberating latent heat) and precipitation falls on the windward side of the range. On the lee side of the mountains the air sinks again and is warmed at the dry adiabatic rate. The air on the lee side of the range is therefore warmer and drier than on the windward side although recent research has suggested that other processes such as air subsidence from the upper troposphere contribute to the warming. Temperatures of $+15°C$ to $+20°C$ have been recorded in winter on the north side of the Alps, accompanied by a relative humidity of only about 10–20%, which has often resulted in catastrophic fires. This warm and dry air with its violent gusts is known in alpine countries as the 'Föhn', a word which is now a generic term in international meteorological language. Föhn weather is associated with wonderfully clear views over long distances. Generally speaking, however, the connection between the weather processes and the air pressure distribution on the weather chart is somewhat loose.

Weather charts, which since 1917 have become more comprehensive, have shown that convergence often leads to the formation of zones with sharp meteorological gradients known as *fronts*. The earliest description and theoretical interpretation of these was made by the great Norwegian physicist Vilhelm Bjerknes and his collaborators. One such front, known as the *polar front*, separates cold *polar* air from warm *subtropical* air. In high pressure areas, where the air is divergent, these air mass boundaries become after a time more or less indistinct.

The concept of air masses as atmospheric regions of rough uniformity and of fronts as the boundaries between air masses (an idea recently superseded by an explanation in more dynamic terms) was accepted by most meteorological services between the two world wars, before regular synoptic aerological readings became generally available. Since then, however, much more information has been available about processes high up in the free atmosphere as well as those over the ground, and this has led to the conclusion that the air mass concept was only partly true. In particular we know today that air masses are no more than areas of slack horizontal gradients and the term can be properly applied only to the lower layers of the atmosphere.

The concept and theory of *fronts* has also changed the original ideas based on a careful analysis of surface weather observations. But recent high level observations have shown that the concept of a front corresponds only loosely to the actual cloud distribution. The original concept of a front was based on the assumption that two air masses of different temperatures travelled towards one another. The warm air then glided over the cold air as soon as the wind increased with height, or the cold air moved into the warm air. The first process produces a *warm front* with a widespread ascent of high, followed by medium, and low clouds which belong in the majority of cases to the group of stable layer clouds. This sequence of cirrostratus-altostratus-nimbostratus clouds is a common event in the middle latitudes, and widespread ice crystal clouds are often followed by snow or rain.

Behind the warm front of a mid-latitude depression (Low) that is,

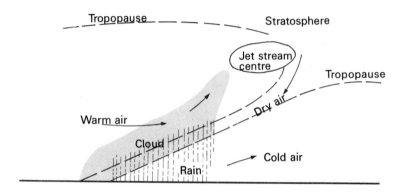

within the warm air of the so-called *warm sector*, we generally find only thin stratus clouds below a low-lying inversion, and practically no clouds at all in the free atmosphere above.

If cold air moves into this warm air, an unstable zone forms very rapidly near its leading edge with numerous towering cumulonimbus clouds, which frequently results in heavy showers. Behind the cold front, there is usually subsidence which produces a small number of billowing clouds, with squally winds, and good visibility. Because of the strong vertical exchange and the strength of the upper winds, this cold front generally moves much faster than the warm front and eventually catches up with it. We then speak of an *occlusion*, from the Latin 'occludere', 'to join together'. The main characteristic of an occlusion is the combination of both types of front. This is the typical form of a mature frontal depression formed in the transition zone between warm and cold air. The wind in a transition zone ('frontal zone') between warm and cold air increases very quickly with height and when the temperature differences are particularly great, *jet streams* will form in the middle and upper troposphere. The greater the temperature difference between two neighbouring air masses, the faster is the jet stream. Such a jet stream is in general characterised by the presence of long parallel streets of middle and high clouds. The velocities within these jet streams can be extraordinarily high – not infrequently as high as 300–400 km/h.

These strong high altitude winds play a very important role in today's intercontinental air traffic in which jet powered aircraft fly at an average speed of 800–900 km/h. The wind velocity within a jet stream decreases very rapidly in all directions away from the centre but particularly in a vertical direction. But although the horizontal and vertical wind shear cannot exceed certain limits it often gives rise to strong turbulence in boundary zones which sometimes shake even large aircraft and have probably been the cause of some air disasters. Since, however, these turbulent zones are usually quite narrow, it is very difficult to predict where they will occur.

The velocity of the jet stream can either increase or decrease in its direction of flow. In a region of wind acceleration or retardation, considerable cross-isobaric air movements take place in accordance with the laws of dynamics. These are deviations of the actual wind from the geostrophic wind determined by the pressure gradient, but they do not amount to more than 5–10%. Nevertheless, these movements of air with their accompanying pressure changes generate cyclones and anticyclones beneath them and so play a very important part in determining the weather. In general the high and low pressure areas in the lower troposphere travel with the air flow but their speed is considerably less than that of higher levels. The movements of pressure formations with the high altitude air flow help us to forecast the weather chart for the following day.

The cyclones and anticyclones of mid-latitudes are almost always complex formations because of the asymmetric distribution of temperature within them. Warm air moves northward, in front of cyclones, and southward behind them. The result is that ascending air, thick cloud and bad weather normally predominate in the front of cyclones, and descending air movements and improving weather predominate in the rear.

Cloud pictures taken from satellites showed for the first time the cloud systems associated with cyclones. They are clearly visible from above but almost always escape the open and uneven network of ground weather stations.

On average, the life of a cyclone is two to three days. The original concept of the Norwegian School of V. Bjerknes was based on the premise that the development of cyclones as wave perturbations and whorls took place continuously along fronts extending right round the world, the polar front in middle latitudes and the arctic front in higher latitudes. However, since about 1938, a three-dimensional study of the atmosphere up to a height of 15–20 km has modified this concept. Air masses close to the ground are constantly changing and frontal zones, jet streams, and fronts develop and decline. New cyclones and anticyclones are developed mainly but by no means wholly by the presence of great movements of air across the isobars. In the entrance area of a jet stream, where the winds are accelerated, anticyclonic cells are built up at the cold, poleward flank. On the warm side, cyclones capable of further development are formed, travel with the high altitude flow and finally shear themselves out of the great westerly air stream as already described. In the delta exit area of jets however, where the velocity of the high altitude wind decreases, the direction of cross-isobaric air movement reverses. The cyclone then becomes deeper on the cold side while the warm high pressure cells simultaneously become stronger.

Cyclones and anticyclones change their thermal structure during their development especially when they are stationary. The constant upward movement in low pressure areas often leads to cooling above and the formation of a cold core which extends over the entire width of a low. Conversely, in high pressure areas the continuous downward movement of air, estimated at about one kilometre a day, causes continuous warming of the atmosphere and they may develop into stationary warm high pressure areas.

Apart from these normal developments there also exist in certain regions more or less permanent cold high pressure cells and warm

48 Cirrus bands over the Red Sea marking position of jet stream.

129

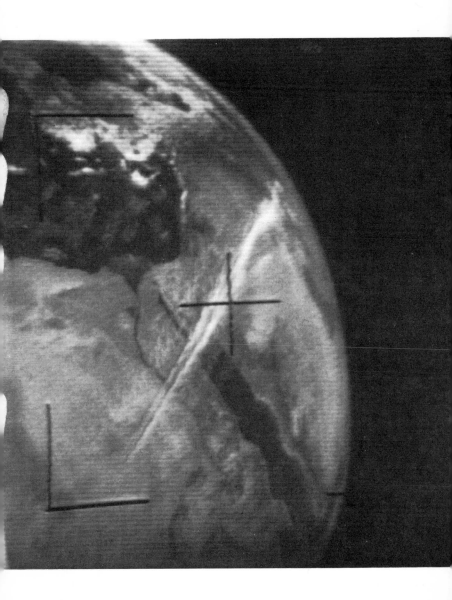

49 Structure of a model occluding depression. *Top row*: horizontal distribution of cloud and precipitation in relation to fronts. *Middle row*: vertical cross-sections along straight lines shown in top row. *Bottom row*: relationship between upper air winds and the surface fronts.

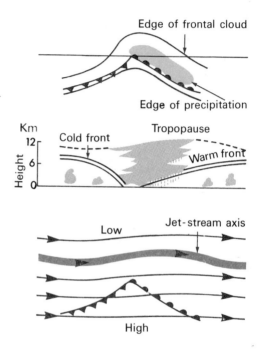

low pressure areas. For instance, we find cold high pressure cells over northern Canada, and over eastern Siberia in winter. Since the pressure of cold air decreases rapidly with height the anticyclonic circulation is replaced at a height of 2–3 km by a cyclonic circulation which increases in intensity with height so that a high level low comes into being over the cold ground. Conversely, in the hottest areas of the continents, such as above Arizona in summer and in north-west India and Iran, we find shallow, persistent low pressure areas on the ground weather chart, but since in warm air decrease of pressure with height is particularly slow, the cyclonic circulation

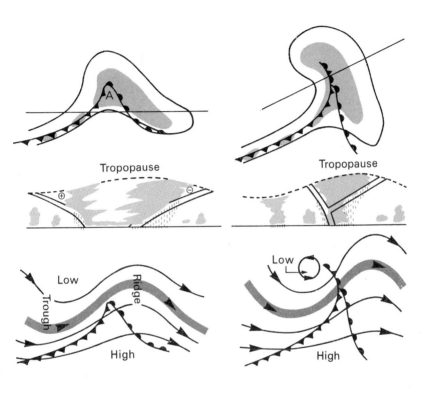

Tropopause

Tropopause

Low

Trough

Ridge

High

Low

High

reverts at heights above 2 to 3 km to an anticyclonic circulation which then extends through the whole troposphere (figure 51).

Warm high pressure cells and cold lows are particularly evident in the areas of the mid-latitude westerlies with their huge meandering oscillations. In certain areas, but especially in the sea areas south of Alaska and along the west coast of Europe, stationary warm anticyclones often form and last for weeks on end; they are common in all seasons in the mid-westerlies at latitudes between 50–60°. When this happens the temperatures are nearly equivalent to those of the tropics, and the tropopause rises

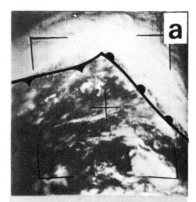

TIROS IV, 807/806, fr 18
1619 GMT, APRIL 5, 1962

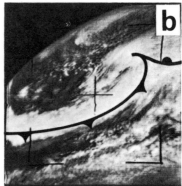

TIROS IV, 894/894, fr 12
1922 GMT, APRIL 11, 1962

TIROS III, 679/678, fr 12
1625 GMT, AUG 28, 1961

TIROS III, 793/792, fr 15
1506 GMT, SEPT 5, 1961

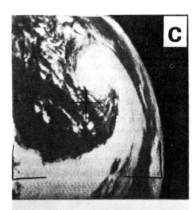

TIROS III, 778/777, fr 16
1357 GMT, SEPT 4,1961

50 Stages in the life cycle of
Northern Hemisphere cyclones.
a Open wave (52°N, 37°W, 1004 mb),
5 April 1962.
b Wave cyclone beginning to occlude
(46°N, 142°W, 1002 mb),
11 April 1962.
c Cyclone 12–18 hours after
occlusion began (48°N, 45°W,
1006 mb), 4 September 1961.
d Deep occluded cyclone near
maximum intensity, 30–60 hours
after occlusion began (51°N, 24°W,
978 mb), 28 August 1961.
e Weakening occluded cyclone,
36–48 hours after occlusion began
(50°N, 45°W, 1006 mb),
5 September 1961.
f Dissipating cyclone, more than
48 hours after occlusion began
(49°N, 4°W, 1009 mb), 19 April 1962.

TIROS IV, 1005/1004,fr 8
1123 GMT, APRIL 19, 1962

51 Schematic cross-section of (**a**) a cold low, intensifying with height, (**b**) a warm high, also intensifying with height, (**c**) a thermal low, and (**d**) a cold high pressure area, the two latter with reverse circulations at high altitude.

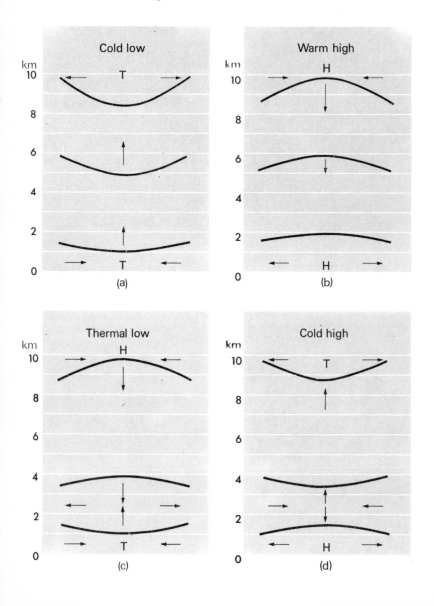

52 A typical synoptic situation for a blocking anticyclone affecting the British Isles.

135

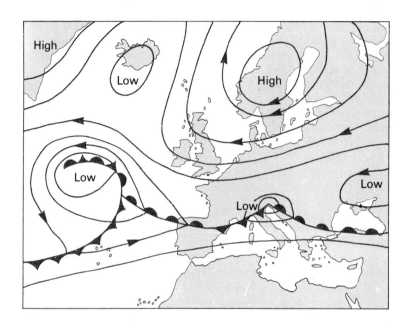

to 13–14 km with temperatures near —78°C. These highs then steer the migrating cyclones either north into the polar zone or south into the subtropics and because of this they are known as *blocking highs*. They are coupled with extensive low pressure troughs in front and behind them which reach deep into the tropics and are associated longitudinally with a succession of cold and warm air streams. Such conditions give rise to weather extremes – unusually cold or warm weather or persistent or heavy precipitation, even in districts that are normally dry. Such conditions occur in all seasons but are particularly common in spring and autumn.

Also noteworthy are the 'cold pools' which may or may not be represented on the surface pressure field. These are high altitude cyclones with a diameter of 500–1,000 km and a core of very cold air in the upper troposphere. They often result in exceptionally low temperatures. For instance the 'cold pool' of 24 January 1941 produced air temperatures in eastern-central Europe lower than the mean temperatures in eastern Siberia. It is a common occurence in a cold winter for one of these 'cold pools' of the troposphere to move into middle latitudes (45–55°). But even in summer isolated 'cold pools' can occur in middle latitudes accompanied almost invariably by considerable vertical instability and frequent thunderstorms, particularly in their rear. 'Cold pools' can occur even in the subtropical latitudes, for instance, in Hawaii or the Azores, also accompanied by unstable cloud formations and widespread rainfall. Their direction of movement depends on the vertically integrated flow and is frequently erratic and difficult to predict. They usually form as a cut-off at the extremity of high amplitude, short wavelength troughs of cold air in the westerlies.

The newly formed cyclones and anticyclones in the extratropical westerly wind belt travel at first with the general air flow in the middle and upper troposphere, like eddies in a river. But some of these whorls develop in such a way that they affect the upper air flow and so make their appearance on upper air charts. Therefore, while in the initial stages of their development these whorls are steered by the upper air flow, they finally come to steer other perturbations.

Local weather prediction is still largely based on ground weather maps, but the interest of meteorologists has shifted more and more to the weather maps of the upper tropopause where pressures are 500 to 200 mb at heights of 5–12 km. At these altitudes are generated the vast meander waves which play such an important part in surface weather processes.

In the *tropical zone* there are various types of perturbation which occur almost exclusively in the lower layers of the atmosphere. Only a few of these develop into vortices, and appear on ground weather maps as cyclones with a shape similar to those of higher latitudes. Most of them are shallow waves travelling from east to west within the tropical easterly current, appearing fairly regularly but especially in undisturbed regions above the sea. Their passage over any particular weather station usually takes 4–5 days. In the front part of these waves there is a component of flow directed towards the equator, where air sinks slowly for dynamic reasons and the trade wind inversion lies very low, so that the clouds are shallow and insignificant. In the northern hemisphere in the region of lowest pressures, there is a convergence of the NE flow of the front part of the wave and the SE flow of the rear of the wave. This convergence, when the air is unstable, easily takes on the character of a cold front, even though the initial temperature differences between the front and rear parts of the wave are only quite small. In the rear of the wave, with one component directed polewards and the same convergence we find the development of strongly billowing clouds accompanied by showers. Although not always clearly recognisable from ground maps, the wave form of this flow is very obvious in the layers between 800 and 600 mb, corresponding to a height of 2–4 km. Sometimes even at these heights there is a closed cyclonic vortex in the centre of such a wave.

Over Africa these wave perturbations migrating from east to west are frequently complicated by a comparatively shallow westerly and therefore contrary air flow in the lower layers of the atmosphere. Under these circumstances a sharp convergence zone forms in the region of the low, leading to severe thunderstorms which in general travel with the overlying easterly upper air flow. If the lower westerly flow becomes very deep, as it does over India where its depth is 4–7 km as opposed to only 1–2 km over the African continent, this leads to the formation of closed low pressure areas which have a tendency to move with the easterly waves and in so doing, to shear out of them towards the poles. The monsoon lows and depressions are the main carriers of precipitation during the summer rainy season in India. If these easterly waves over the ocean, like the continental monsoon lows, reach

53 Surface chart showing a model of a wave in the tropical easterlies (pressure in millibars). A section through **A–B** is shown opposite.
54 Vertical section of an easterly wave model. The upper limit of the moist layer is dashed. Weather symbols are shown below.

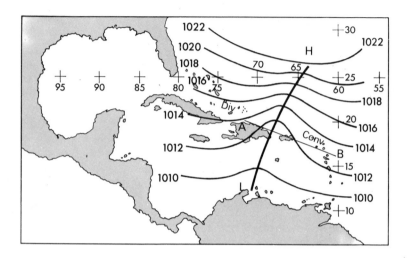

the region of the migrating upper lows of the westerlies, they are frequently reinforced and steered polewards. Interaction then takes place between the high-lying offshoots of the westerlies and the tropical perturbations and they combine in vast systems in the transition zone between the tropics and the subtropics, accompanied mostly by extremely heavy precipitation.

On the other hand the weather conditions associated with a low pressure area are often absent when an anticyclonic flow overlies the heat lows mentioned earlier on. In spite of converging winds in the lower layers, no clouds of any importance form, nor is there any precipitation, because the air in this arid region is so dry that the dew-point, and therefore the condition for cloud formation, is not reached at heights below 4–5 km.

Tropical hurricanes deserve special attention because they are perhaps the most impressive meteorological phenomena close to the earth's surface. 'Hurricane' is derived from the Mexican word 'hurrikan' meaning gale or severe storm. Tropical hurricanes

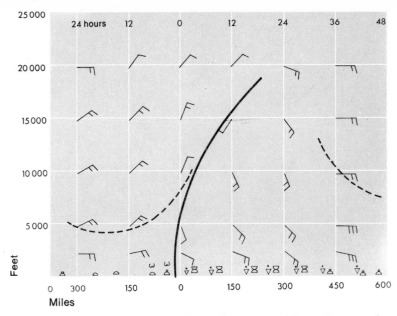

Key: ϙ̇ rain showers   ꒰ altocumulus   ꒱ fair weather cumulus

       Ɣ̃ cumulonimbus   ꙮ cumulus with vertical growth

occur mainly in the late summer or autumn in the tropical zone of the oceans, but not within 5° of the equator. This is because near the equator the deflecting force of the earth's rotation is practically zero and any pressure differences that may arise are immediately neutralised by winds blowing from high to low pressure. So far very little is known about the early stages of the development of a tropical hurricane. Obviously, however, very few tropical cyclones reach the full intensity of a hurricane. In contrast with the process in the central lows in the higher latitudes a warm core forms in a fully developed hurricane, with downward movements of air accompanied by the dissipation of clouds. This core is known as the 'eye' of the hurricane. The 'eye' has a diameter of between 20–50 km and temperatures which in the middle layers are about 10–18°C higher than their surroundings. This practically cloud-free area is surrounded by a giant amphitheatre of cloud systems which can reach up to the tropical tropopause at about 17 km. The highest wind velocities occur along the periphery of this cloud

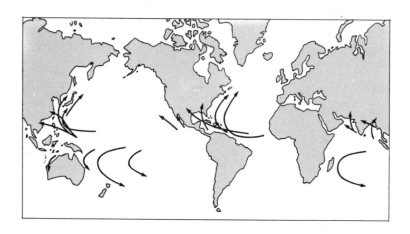

ring, sometimes reaching 200 km/h; on one occasion 500 km/h was recorded before the instruments were destroyed. Hurricane-like gales, high seas, and deluges of rain often result in fatal catastrophes. In the closely populated flat delta area of the Ganges and the Brahmaputra no fewer than 250,000 people lost their lives in 1876 when a tidal wave caused by a tropical hurricane raised the water level of these rivers by 12 metres. The outer area of tropical hurricanes is characterised by spiralling streets of billowing cloud, with a diameter of 300 km, and reaching great altitudes. A dense umbrella of ice crystal cloud stretches to a diameter of 600–800 km from the storm centre.

Hurricanes can last over the tropical oceans for 2–3 weeks, moving with the easterly upper air flow towards the west and gradually shearing away polewards. In the front part of an upper trough of the westerlies they are steered rapidly poleward and drawn into the extratropical westerly stream. Colder air sometimes forces its way into these areas and gradually transforms a warm cyclone into an extratropical cyclone with a warm and a cold front. As soon as they move over land, however, surface friction

56 Section through a tropical cyclone showing the horizontal and vertical wind components. The rain belts correspond to the spiralling bands of cumulonimbus seen in figure 57.

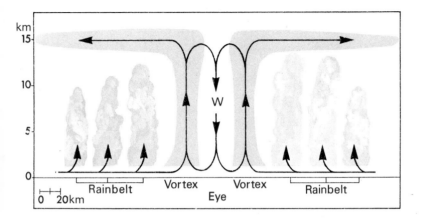

makes the airflow more centripetal and the upward movement of the air is intensified. This leads to a rapid filling up of the cyclone and at the same time to disastrous rainfalls.

We are indebted to the hurricane research centre of the US Weather Bureau in Miami, Florida, for a comprehensive survey of the processes by which hurricanes are formed, processes which involve the greatest transformation of energy now known to us. The terrific wind velocities of 50–100 m/s, that is, 180–360 km/h, whip up the surface of the oceans and increase tenfold the normal transmission of sensible and latent heat into the air. Only a small part of the energy liberated in the clouds by condensation is converted into the kinetic energy of the wind. The remaining and greater portion is converted into the potential energy of the air through its pressure distribution. A tropical hurricane with its warm core, in contrast with most extratropical cyclones, uses heat like a heat engine. It produces kinetic energy at the rate of about 10^{12} kilowatt hours per day – more energy than is produced by man over the whole globe! Although the annual average of fully developed hurricanes is only about sixty, 75% of them in the

57 Tropical cyclone over the Arabian Sea.

Northern Hemisphere, they make a considerable contribution to the energy budget and also to the water budget of the whole atmosphere.

These tropical hurricanes must not be confused with tornadoes or whirlwinds, which are small vortices with a diameter of at the most a few hundred metres and consist of a column of revolving air with very low pressure at its centre causing a spiralling pillar of cloud to project downward from the mother cloud. They are identical with the waterspouts seen occasionally over the sea. They rarely occur in Europe but are quite frequent in North America, particularly in spring. Their wind velocities within relatively narrow limits reach 200–400 km/h and can cause tremendous damage, although the greatest devastation occurs when buildings literally 'explode' beneath their low-pressure centres.

American weather satellites, which have circled the earth since 1961 with very few interruptions, have brought us new insights into the special distribution and disposition of the clouds. From a height of 200–700 km they can overlook areas of several million square kilometres and send back television pictures showing cells, lanes, or spiral cloud systems. Tropical and extratropical cyclones are usually easy to recognise as whorls and their position can be determined without difficulty; but there are sometimes surprising results such as the discovery that the life of some circulation spirals can be very long. Before satellite observations, many perturbations in the tropical zone escaped the wide-meshed weather station network, but they can now be kept under constant surveillance. The great jet streams generally reveal themselves by the presence of extended cloud lanes in the middle and higher layers. High pressure zones are either cloudless or else contain cellular cloud systems. With some experience all this information can be used to determine the wind distribution.

Apart from providing photographs of clouds, satellites will now be able to make infra-red measurements of the radiation temperature of the cloud surfaces as well as the earth's surface and this information will be extremely valuable. It will give us a

58 *Below* Nimbostratus over northern Germany, the Baltic Sea and Poland, with warm front cirrus streamers above the Bay of Biscay and France. In the north-west is cellular cumulus and stratocumulus in unstable cold air, and a weak disturbance in the western Mediterranean. The Alps and hills of southern Germany and Czechoslovakia are covered with snow, anticyclonic conditions prevail, and there is a sun glint in the Gulf of Genoa. (21 March 1964).

59 *Right* An infra-red picture (about 23h local time) of the southern Indian Ocean. At lower left are frontal clouds, and at the bottom they partially hide the margin of the Antarctic ice-cap. Cellular clouds are in the centre (35–50°S), with low-level stratocumulus at 20–25°S.

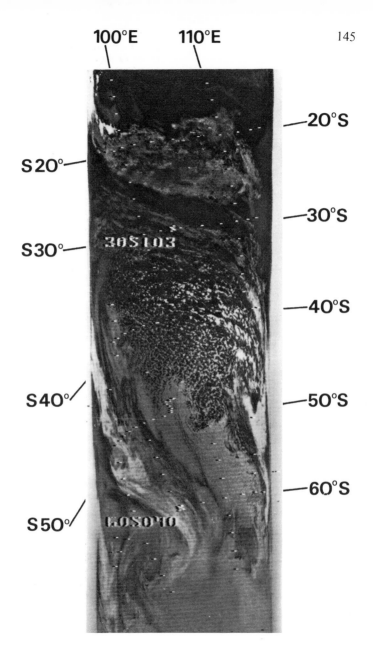

146

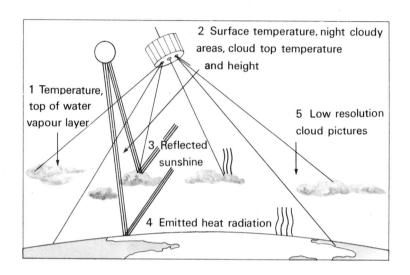

1 Temperature, top of water vapour layer

2 Surface temperature, night cloudy areas, cloud top temperature and height

5 Low resolution cloud pictures

3 Reflected sunshine

4 Emitted heat radiation

measure of the height of the upper surfaces of the clouds. Such measurements, particularly those taken at night, enable satellites, which only take about 100 minutes to encircle the earth to keep a constant check on the course of the weather. Weather forecasters will obviously have to learn how to interpret the information supplied by this wonderful new aid, and indeed difficulties have already arisen in the recognition of cloud forms on the photographs taken by the satellite *Tiros*. The axis of rotation of the first of the *Tiros* satellites, *Tiros* I–X, was designed to keep constant in space. But this made the time during which the earth's surface could be observed too short, since it depended on the position of the camera axis and the illumination of the earth's surface. On the other hand, the *Nimbus* satellite which was tested in 1964 had cameras and radiation recorders which always pointed towards the earth's surface. This enabled a continuous watch to be maintained. The

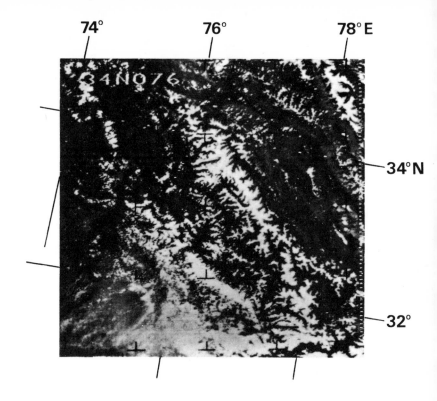

lenses of the television cameras have an amazing power of resolution but unfortunately this is partly lost in the reproduction of the pictures.

It is particularly important for the future development of this science that satellites provided with high resolution lenses are able to make accurate radiation measurements in various parts of the spectrum, to ascertain for instance, the albedo of the short-wave radiation and long-wave infra-red radiation. In the 'window' from $8–12\mu$ where water-vapour is completely transparent to radiation, it is possible to measure the effective radiation temperature of the surface of the clouds and of the earth. These measurements provide an impressive picture of the distribution of the clouds at night. In other parts of the spectrum it is possible to measure the radiation absorbed and emitted by water-vapour or carbon dioxide. This in turn enables us to obtain information on the water-vapour content and the temperature of the upper troposphere. It will now be possible, for the first time, to measure and observe continuously the chief individual terms of the radiation budget.

Weather prediction, as has been said already, is based on recording the atmospheric conditions over large areas and ideally over a whole hemisphere at a particular moment. If we have this information we can then estimate the speed and the direction in which individual cyclones, anticyclones, fronts, and bad weather areas will move. The time factor involved is very difficult to estimate and requires a great deal of experience and much intuition on the part of the forecaster. Cyclones and anticyclones grow and decline, fronts merge or dissolve and die out, bad weather areas appear or disappear. All these changes occur so rapidly that a prediction of weather conditions beyond 48 hours is practically impossible, but for the first 24–36 hours prediction charts usually give very satisfactory results. Predictions for 3–6 days can give only very general indications of the weather over a large area. But it is quite impossible with this method to make long-range predictions covering months or years.

The empirical methods previously used in weather prediction have undoubtedly reached the limit of their reliability and cannot be appreciably improved by any sort of refinement in technique. One reason for this is that these methods include many subjective parameters, such as experience and intuition, which can never be entirely reliable. On the other hand the macro-processes in the atmosphere are largely determined by physical laws and it is proving increasingly possible, with the help of basic physical equations, to compute a future condition of the atmosphere on the basis of a known state, and therefore to predict the weather associated with it. A beginning was made early this century by V. Bjerknes, in 1904, who postulated for the first time the hypothesis that accurate weather prediction could be based on physical mathematics. This hypothesis could not be verified in the first experiments. But the development of electronic computors since the end of the last war has made it possible to aim once more at Bjerknes's objective. It was Carl-Gustav Rossby, the meteorologist, and John von Neumann, the mathematician, with a small number of highly talented collaborators in the United States, who ventured into this new territory again in 1949.

Their first results were so impressive, in spite of some weak points, that after some years, all the important weather services adopted their method of analysing and predicting the weather. This involved the application of simplified forms of fundamental physical equations representing atmospheric equilibrium and atmospheric movements. In the model of the atmosphere used in this method, some important processes are still not included, but all the same the results obtained are in remarkably good agreement with actual observations. The continuous fields of the atmosphere (wind, temperature, and so on) are represented on a network of grid points, which because of the size of the area involved are separated from one another by 200–300 km, while vertically, one or two, or at most five layers have to suffice. Basic differential equations are then applied to observations at the network of grid points and their solution, which takes only a few minutes, is embodied in a weather prediction map covering 12, 24 or 48 hours.

A critical comparison of weather prediction maps obtained with the help of computers and those derived empirically has shown that both techniques give, at the present time, roughly comparable results. But the utilisation of increasingly efficient computers and increasingly accurate models will greatly improve this technique, whereas the empirical method has reached its limits, at least in principle. One of the great advantages of the quantitative approach is that it appreciably increases the speed at which predictions can be made. Even the first step – the analysis of the state of the atmosphere at any given moment – can be taken by a computer and worked out automatically with full objectivity. If we look at the whole system of equations, referring to several thousand grid points in each of two to five layers one above the other, then we see that for a 24-hour weather forecast the number of operations required is from 10^7 to 10^8. The mathematical prediction of weather requires the use of computers with the highest available speed and storage capacity.

In the mathematical methods used at present several important processes occuring within the atmosphere are not taken into account, among them being the differential heating and cooling process in space and regional differences in ground surface friction. On the other hand the effect of mountain ranges is taken into account. Many local effects dependent on the nature of the surface of the ground are also neglected and it is therefore not surprising that ground surface maps constructed in this way are less accurate than upper air maps. A remarkable result is that they disregard fronts (not frontal zones!), but this has no effect at all on the formation and movement of cyclones and waves. However, the weather prediction models used at present do not permit meteorologists to make instant weather predictions: they must still interpret the results obtained. A significant improvement in the mathematical prediction of weather conditions requires the construction of more comprehensive models of the atmosphere which represent more accurately and more completely the physical processes that occur there, and fully utilise all the data available, including that from satellites. In effect, this means increasing the efficiency of computers and this is what is happening now.

In the present state of the science, however, as well as in the foreseeable future, prediction will necessarily be restricted to those processes in the atmosphere which involve movements on a large scale. The reason for this is mainly that it is not possible to increase the space and time coverage of the aerological stations beyond a certain limit. At present the distance between the points where aerological ascents are made above land is about 250–300 km, and up to 1,000 km above the sea in the Northern Hemisphere, the time interval being in general 12 hours. Many minor and temporary phenomena obviously escape such a network. This applies particularly to the important early stages of such phenomena. In addition, insufficient quantitative information is available on the basic processes of heating and cooling, and especially on radiation processes, and processes of the water budget (precipitation and evaporation). Some of these processes can now be studied with the help of meteorological satellites. But others, particularly the hydrological processes which are so important in the energy balance, cannot be studied by this method. However, a completely new observation system called 'World Weather Watch' is now in preparation. This is based on a series of balloons which will be allowed to drift freely with the wind at various heights. The measurements recorded by them will be transmitted continuously to communication satellites which will then retransmit them to meteorological centres.

But in spite of all these possibilities, the efficiency of mathematical weather prediction will always remain limited for technical reasons. This applies particularly to the time factor; predictions beyond two or three days will be extended only with great difficulty. The problem involved is primarily a practical one concerning the recording of information and the instruments themselves. The problems are basically soluble, of course, but only at a cost of considerable technical and financial investment. Beyond this there are also the basic physical problems of the atmosphere which are perhaps completely insoluble. This raises doubts as to the possibility of our ever achieving accurate long-range forecasting over, say, a whole year. We know that in the atmosphere processes involving orders of magnitude ranging from a few millimetres to thousands of kilometres, take place side by side. We do not know yet, however, to what extent the small-scale processes, that is, processes involving small volumes of space which escape all observation networks, influence the processes involving large masses of air. From what order of magnitude downwards can the smaller processes be neglected? How does the interaction of the processes of various orders of magnitude proceed? What quantitative role, for instance, do the microphysical processes in the clouds play during the formation of precipitation and the development of frontal zones and cyclones? The answers to all of these questions still rely upon unproved assumptions.

But even if we restrict ourselves to processes involving large air masses, we meet basic physical difficulties. We have already learned that the atmosphere can be unstable in several ways. There is, for instance, vertical thermodynamic instability. In such zones it is impossible to localise the place and time at which a thunderstorm cell develops. We can only predict where there will be a general tendency towards thunderstorms. The dynamic instability of the upper air flow, particularly in the region of the jet streams, is even more far reaching in its effect. The horizontal shear of the wind can reach such a high value on the warm anticyclonic side of a jet stream that an accidental deviation caused by the development of cumulonimbus clouds or the effect of mountain barriers can no longer be damped and will grow in size to the dimensions of cyclones and anticyclones. Such a process is obviously involved in the formation of new cyclones and anticyclones, at least in extreme cases; in such cases, however, it is theoretically impossible to predict the time and place where new large cyclones will form because these factors are influenced by random events on a smaller scale. Yet this is the principal task of weather prediction!

If a weather situation is being influenced by small-scale events, then the various instabilities of the atmosphere will set a time limit to our predictions. These difficulties cannot be overcome by even the most efficient weather observation grids or mathematical techniques. Experience will tell us whether these basic objections are justified or whether they are problems which technical progress will solve.

Another justifiable objection is that the calculations relate only to one section of the atmosphere when in fact they should include the whole of our globe. For short term predictions in middle latitudes we can however ignore the events that occur in the tropical zone which, though they involve huge quantities of energy, do not have an immediate effect upon the weather elsewhere.

The use of new observation techniques such as radar and satellites and new mathematical methods has given an amazing impetus to weather forecasting. In the next few years we can expect a marked improvement in medium-range macro-scale forecasting. But to be able to predict the weather at a particular place and time, weeks or even months in advance, is not likely to be possible in the foreseeable future for technical, financial, and probably basic physical reasons.

5 Climate and climatic zones

5 Climate and climatic zones

Climate was traditionally defined as the average state of the atmosphere over, say, 30–50 years. But such a definition is neither very informative nor complete because it does not take into account the constant variations of weather. Yet it is these variations which typify not only the climate in Europe but that in other climatic zones. We should think of climate, therefore, as the sum of weather variations.

The concept of climate generally refers to the normal or mean course of the weather. If we want to describe the climate of a particular place quantitatively we need to know not only the mean temperature, precipitation and winds, but also when and where these were obtained. In addition we need information on air pressure, the moisture in the atmosphere, the incidence of cloud, hours of sunshine, the visibility, the snow cover, and so on, all of which have to be considered statistically. That is, we need to know the distribution of individual values as well as their mean. Represented on maps and atlases, this information enables us to make quantitative comparisons between various areas such as the annual rainfall for a given period. If we plot, for instance, the mean temperature over running 30 year periods, we at once become aware of climatic variations which in some areas can be very considerable. It is therefore unavoidable to use data only for the same time period so as to make all figures directly comparable.

The climate of an area depends then on a number of factors. These are its latitude, its altitude, and its proximity to the sea, lakes and mountains. If we consider local differences in climate, we find that other factors also come into play. These are the inclination and aspect of slopes; the vegetation, which is itself influenced very strongly by the climate; and the nature of the ground surface. To the physicist, however, all these are but the external manifestations of climatic factors. Local climate is in fact governed by the various factors of the radiation and heat budget and the water budget. Particularly important are global radiation $(S + H)$, the albedo, and the radiation balance Q on the one hand, and on the other, the duration of flow of sensible heat (T_L) and latent heat of water-vapour (T_V) from the earth's surface to the air or vice versa. The greater the proportion of T_L in the available energy Q, the higher the temperature during the day. In dry climates which are rich in radiation almost the entire incoming solar energy is used to warm the air. But in the arid desert areas of northern Chile and Iran, where the nocturnal transmission of radiation is also very strong, the mean difference between the maximum day temperatures and the minimum night temperatures can rise to 25–30°C or more. Over the seas a great deal of radiation energy is used for evaporation. The balance is stored in the water which is subjected to thorough mixing by the ever-present winds. T_L is then very small and the daily variation of temperature is reduced to a few tenths of a degree.

Any change of weather, however, greatly influences the values of the heat budget factors. This is because the airstreams carried by the great wind currents are subject to great variation in their amount of cloud, temperature and transparency to radiation. We call the processes involving the transfer of heat by the horizontal movement of air, *advection*. Advection often plays a much more important part in temperate climate zones, such as western and northern Europe, than the local heat budget. The relation between the heat budget terms and the advection terms has been determined only for temperature in a few places. In a climate in which there is no advection (a theoretical concept) the heat budget alone, which is dependent on radiation laws, would dictate temperature variations. There would be a uniform pattern, influenced only by seasonal variations in the elevation of the sun. Variations of the weather on any particular day in such a region would then be regarded as deviations from an average monthly mean. It has been shown that variations due to advection near Berlin in the summer amount to 37–39% but in the winter to as much as 74–85%. In Africa during the dry period the figures are 5–10% whereas on high mountain peaks they are 80–90%.

Figure 8 showed how the mean temperature for entire parallels in the (a) summer and (b) winter months depends on the geographic

Table 5 Resultant upper winds, Hanover (Germany) 1961–1965. (180° = S, 270° = W)

Altitude	January Direction	Speed	Constancy
30 km	–	–	–
25	293°	25 m/s	91%
20	285°	22	88
16	289°	17	85
12	302°	12	65
10	307°	12	50
8	315°	11	42
5	308°	8·2	44
3	296°	6·1	43
1	269°	5·1	42
Surface	228°	2·3	43

latitude. Temperatures in the Northern Hemisphere are in general a little higher, about 2° on average, than in the Southern Hemisphere. The mean air temperature for the whole globe is about 15°C.

The mean annual temperature is between 26–28°C in the equatorial zone, −48°C at the South Pole, and as low as −56°C over the centre of the ice-cap in that region, as compared with −17°C at the North Pole. All this, however, leaves out of account the enormous influence of the disposition of land and sea on our globe. The most striking example of this is illustrated by a comparison of the mean temperatures of the Faroe Islands (hottest month +11°C, coldest month +3·7°C), and Yakutsk in eastern Siberia (July +19·5°C, January −43°C), both lying at latitude 62°N.

July

Direction	Speed	Constancy
104°	12 m/s	97%
98°	8	98
119°	2	55
257°	5	78
276°	12	72
278°	15	69
274°	14	70
269°	10	75
265°	8·2	77
264°	6·0	72
248°	2·6	63

The west coasts in the westerly wind zone have an equable maritime climate with mild winters and cool summers, whereas the east coasts have a continental climate with very cold winters. The lower temperatures along the east coasts are partly due to the presence of cold polar winds on the western side of mid-tropospheric troughs of low pressure, and partly also to the wind-driven cold currents of the oceanic general circulation.

We know that up to heights of 2,000 m, temperature generally decreases with height by an average of about 5°C per 1,000 m. At greater altitudes and in arid zones this vertical decrease rises to 6–7°C. There are however large areas including the polar regions, the subpolar continent areas when they are covered with snow, and certain mountain hollows during the winter, where the daily mean temperature increases with height, forming a temperature inversion. The highest temperatures in these areas are often recorded between 800 and 1,200 m, where a high-lying fog belt or a sharply bounded mist blanket separates the cold, stable, lower cold air from the dry, warm, sinking air above associated with good visibility. Such an inversion regularly makes its appearance, for instance, in winter in the eastern Alps in the basin of Klagenfurt where the mean January temperature is about −5·5°C, whereas at heights between 800–1,000 m the mean temperature is −2·8°C. The mean temperature at a height between 1,500–2,000 m in the winter in eastern Siberia is about −26°C with only slight regional variations, whereas the medium values in the valleys of Ojmjakon and Verkhojansk sink to −47°C. The lowest mean temperatures associated with such inversions have been recorded over the ice-covered inland regions of the Antarctic. The weather station Sowjetskaia recorded a mean annual temperature of −56°C at an altitude of 3,570 m. The mean reading for the warmest month, December, was −33°C, and for May to September, that is, during the winter, −69°C, with a record low reading of about −88°C which has been repeated several times since then. Inversions, at altitudes between 1,000–2,000 m, also occur extensively in the trade wind areas over the sea. Under these circumstances, however, the temperature at first decreases with height in the lower currents of the trade wind as a result of vigorous mixing and the supply of heat from the ground.

The highest mean summer temperatures of 37–38°C occur in the extensive desert belt of the Sahara, over Arabia and southern Iran to the Indus. The highest figures ever recorded are about 55°C but the accuracy of some readings is a little suspect owing to the difficulties of avoiding the direct effects of solar radiation. In Sibi (Baluchistan), the mean nocturnal minimum temperature in June and July does not fall below +31°C. Human beings, however, tolerate these high desert temperatures when they are coupled with relative humidities of 30–50% at night and less than 10% during the day, much more easily than the humid, sweltering heat of the coastal regions of the Persian Gulf or the Red Sea, where the temperatures range from 34–36°C, but where the relative humidity is about 70%. In the shallow Persian Gulf the mean water temperature near the shore is about 36°C. In Europe, experienced mothers would hesitate to bathe their babies in such 'hot' water!

The distribution of precipitation is subject to great local as well as regional variations. Apart from the general circulation of the atmosphere which creates climate, local influences play a very important role in this process. If a mountain range forces air masses to ascend, cooling takes place and when the dew-point is reached, there is condensation and cloud formation, even outside migrating cyclonic perturbations. The greater the amount of moisture present in the air and the higher the air rises, the greater, of course, is the formation of cloud. So on the windward side of mountain ranges there is frequently an accumulation of cloud and intensification of precipitation depending on the strength of the prevailing wind. The greatest mean annual precipitation, 10–12 m, has been recorded under such conditions on the windward side of tropical and subtropical mountain ranges such as the Cameroon Mountains, on the west coast of Colombia and the Khasi Mountains in Assam. The weather station of Waialeale – this onomatopoeic word means 'running water' – measured a mean precipitation record of 1,248 cm a year over 39 years at a height of about 1,300 m. In Cherrapunji, on the slopes of the Khasi Mountains in Assam, a precipitation total of over 22 m was recorded for 1861. Rainfall in this region occurs almost exclusively during the warm season. The mean rainfall in June and July is 250–280 cm each, which is equivalent to the total rainfall for 4–5 years in Paris, London or Berlin. A day without rain is something quite unknown during this period of summer deluges*.

* It should be mentioned in this connection that the greatest amount of precipitation ever recorded in 24 hours was on the Island of Reunion. The amount was 187 cm on 16.3.52. The greatest amount of precipitation R for a given point is obtained by the application of the formula $R = 422 \times D^{0.48}$, where R is expressed in mm and D, the duration of the precipitation, in hours.

On the other hand, there are regions in which there has been no measurable precipitation for many years and even for decades. An extreme example of this is the Atacama desert in northern Chile, where salts like saltpetre which are easily soluble in water have lain for thousands of years on the surface of the ground. But even in Luxor, in Aswan in upper Egypt, and in Hurgada on the Red Sea, the mean annual precipitation amounts to only 1–4 mm, and in the huge regions of the central Sahara, in central Iran, and on the west coast of Peru it amounts to less than 20 mm. A precipitation of 1 mm of rain is equivalent to 1 litre of water per square metre.

Precipitation is generally greater over land than over the neighbouring sea, because there is greater mechanical and thermal overturning of the air over the land. Again, in all cyclonic perturbations, the ground winds are steered more towards the centre of the low as it moves over the land, with its greater surface friction, and this increases the vertical ascent of air.

The duration and frequency of precipitation is more important to city dwellers than its amount. Precipitation is particularly frequent on the west coasts of temperate latitudes where high mountain ranges force the prevailing winds to ascend. An example of this is the island of Evangelistas in southern Chile where it rains on average 305 days a year, compared with 0·5 days per year in Aswan.

For most vegetation, including grazing land without artificial irrigation, it is the relationship between the amount of precipitation and evaporation which is significant rather than the amount of precipitation alone. We have already discussed the important difference between the actual and the potential evaporation in chapter 1. For vegetation and the water budget of a dry region the actual evaporation is less important than the potential evaporation, however strange this may appear. If we disregard the possible replacement of evaporated water by ground water or artificial irrigation, then the actual evaporation can never be greater than the amount of precipitation.

On the other hand, open areas of surface water and well watered arable or grass land with ground water not far below the surface, give the maximum possible amount of evaporation. The actual amount depends mainly on the energy made available by the radiation balance, the variation of the moisture in the air with height (components Q and T_V of the water budget), and the advection of dry air. This process of advection plays a particularly important part, for instance, in oases where the constantly blowing dry hot desert air provides additional energy which is then cooled on the surface of the water. The result is that the potential evaporation from a water hole in the desert may be as much as 4 cm per day. The energy required for this is 2,400 Ly/d which is much greater than the maximum amount of insolation.

The almost unlimited variety of climates that exists on our globe needs classification into groups. Many suggestions for this have been made, some of them going back to ancient history. The Greeks, for instance, spoke of climate as being divided into three zones: a torrid zone, a temperate zone, and a frigid zone. Climatic classifications can however be divided into two main groups: a genetic group, based on the cause of climates, and an 'effective' or 'applied' classification, based on the effects of climate, for instance, on the natural vegetation, or the water budget. The latter is much more important from the practical point of view, and involves temperature limits, or the relationship between precipitation and evaporation. It also includes classifications based on specific effects such as those of special interest to medicine or industry. We will return to this second classification later in this chapter.

If, however, we want to understand the geographical distribution of the world's climates, we must understand their origins. The fundamental causes of climate are the seasonal and geographical variations in the amounts of radiation striking the earth, the inclination (about 23°) of the earth's axis of rotation to a vertical drawn through the plane of its orbit round the sun, and the general circulation of the earth's atmosphere. This circulation is due to the latitudinal and seasonal variation in the distribution of radiation and heat.

In chapter 3 we looked at the great pressure and wind belts of the

earth's atmosphere and their seasonal movements. These movements are quite small over the sea, where 85–90% of the energy of
the radiation balance is used for evaporation, as demonstrated in
the central Pacific. Over land, on the other hand, where the major
part of the radiation energy is available for the direct heating of
air, the seasonal variations of radiation can have a much more
direct effect (see figure 6). Over land the great pressure and wind
systems of the tropical and subtropical zones move with the
vertical position of the sun. This is illustrated by what occurs over
Africa, which is arranged more or less symmetrically about the
equator. The equatorial low pressure zone moves from 17–18°N in
the northern summer (July and August), to about 20°S in the
southern summer (January and February). This movement is even
more marked over southern Asia, the largest of all continents, where
the northernmost cell of the intertropical convergence zone in
the Punjab regularly moves to 28–30°N (figure 43). Here the
heating of the air in summer is further increased by the highlands
of Tibet of which almost two million km² lie at an average altitude
of 4,500 m, above which the highest mean temperatures are found
in the troposphere.

The subtropical high pressure cells disappear in summer over
this continent as a result of the overheating of the air which
promotes the development of shallow thermal lows. But in all
upper-air weather maps, they appear as unusually persistent and
strong warm cells whose axis shifts with height towards the
equator. For this reason the subtropical high pressure cells are
subject to very little seasonal variation, the movement from
summer to winter being equivalent to only about 5–10° latitude.
In these high pressure cells, the air subsides and diverges near the
ground. The weather is dry and the skies generally clear. It is
thus possible for the extratropical west winds to reach further
towards the equator in the winter than in the summer. All these
movements of the great wind belts, as a result of the seasonal
storage of heat in the sea and the atmosphere, take place with a lag
behind the vertical sun of about 4–6 weeks, or more than two

months over the seas. The extremes occur around January and February, and July and August. In the spring months of March and April the atmospheric circulation still corresponds to winter conditions, whereas in the autumn month of September it corresponds, though not quite so closely, to summer conditions.

In the Southern Hemisphere where the Antarctic continent is effectively isolated from other continents, the circulation belts are subject to only small seasonal shifts in position. We have already seen that Antarctica receives its maximum radiation in the southern summer, when the distance between the earth and the sun is at its minimum, but this has little effect because of the high albedo of the snow-covered ice sheet. The situation, however, is quite different in the Northern Hemisphere where the Arctic Ocean, covered by a permanent layer of ice, is surrounded by great continents which are heated considerably in the summer months and lose their snow even in the subpolar zone (65–75°N). The major part of the radiation striking the Arctic Ocean in the summer is used to melt the surface of the ice floes.

In winter, the subpolar depressions move towards the inner Arctic as the result of the small surface friction and the constant supply of heat through the thin ice cover of the sea, whereas in summer they more frequently move towards the centre of the warm continents. So in summer, in the Northern Hemisphere, the subpolar low pressure zone moves towards the south, whereas in winter it moves polewards to above the Arctic Ocean. The direction of this seasonal movement is therefore opposite to that in the tropical zone. Low pressure zones travel towards continents in the warm summer season and towards warmer oceans in winter.

We have already seen in chapter 3 that the seasonal variation of air movements close to the ground in some regions results in a change or even a complete reversal in direction of the prevailing winds. Table 4 gives an overall picture of global air pressure and wind belts over the oceans. In continental regions the equatorial westerly wind zone, which we have already discussed, has to be added. These belts move with the vertical sun and, as we have already seen, the movements are much greater over the land than over the sea. The warmest zone and with it the thermal lows of the intertropical convergence zone shift in summer to near the tropics (23·5° latitude). If we disregard isolated occurrences, which are often confusing, we see that the prevailing weather belts move with these pressure and wind belts. The result is thick clouds and frequent precipitation in low pressure zones and also, to a lesser degree, in the westerly wind belts, and clear skies and mainly dry weather in the region of the high pressure cells and to some extent in the easterly wind belts.

We cannot go further here into the statistical relationship between wind direction and weather, a relationship which applies only to the mean and not to single cases. The simplest explanation is that the vertical factors of the Coriolis force tend to produce a downward movement in the east winds and an upward movement in the west winds, but near the poles this force disappears.

Over the oceans like the Pacific there are no sharp seasonal differences in weather because the migratory movement of the wind belts is very small. On the continents, however, and particularly in the region including Africa, Asia, Australia and the continentally influenced Indian Ocean, great differences do exist, as shown in the purposely schematic classification in table 7. The latitudes given are only approximate as there are considerable individual variations because of the distribution of land and sea, great mountain ranges, and ocean currents.

Over the great oceans seasonal contrasts are very limited in size both laterally and vertically, and sometimes do not exist at all between the subtropical winter rainy zone and the tropical summer rainy zone. The boundaries of the subtropical dry zones are also somewhat vague because the subtropical high pressure cells are constantly growing and declining, as well as travelling, sometimes over a long period. This is the reason why the trade wind zone is very dry: for instance, on the island of Ascension (8°S) in the middle of the Atlantic, the annual mean rainfall amounts to only 65 mm. Over the southern Atlantic and southern

Table 6 Mean temperature on the west and east coasts of the continents at a latitude of 48°N

	Warmest month	Coldest month	Year
West coast of North America Tattosh Island, Washington D.C.	+10·9°C	+4·9°C	+8·1°C
East coast of North America St John's, Newfoundland	+15·4°C	−5·6°C	+4·8°C
West coast of Europe Brest, France	+17·0°C	+7·1°C	+11·6°C
East coast of Asia Otiai, Sakhalin	+16·5°C	−16·0°C	+1·3°C

Table 7 Climatic zones and the atmospheric circulation in continental regions

1	**High polar zone**	80–90°N, 70–90°S	Little precipitation all the year round, variable winds, predominantly east.
2	**Subpolar zone**	60–80°N, 55–70°S	Thick cloud and heavy precipitation all the year round, strong variable winds.
3	**Temperate zone**	40–60°N, 35–55°S	Varying amount of cloud and moderate precipitation all the year round, prevailing winds from the west.
4	**Subtropical winter rainy zone**	30–40°N, 30–35°S	Predominantly in the western region of the continents; fine and dry weather in the summer, winds mostly weak; varying cloud cover and precipitation in the winter, prevailing westerly winds.
5	**Subtropical dry zone**	20–30°N, 20–30°S	Absent in the eastern portion of the continents, fine all the year round with weak and dry winds.
6	**Tropical summer rainy zone**	10–20°N, 5–20°S	In the summer cloudy with showers, variable winds, westerly according to regions; fine and dry winters, trade winds from the east.
7	**Equatorial rainy zone**	5°S–10°N	Very cloudy all the year round, thundery showers, weak variable winds, mostly from the west.

62 Climatic arrangement in the eastern equatorial Pacific. The line is the average boundary between the dry trade wind climate to the south and the moist equatorial zone to the north. Rainfall increases fairly rapidly northwards.

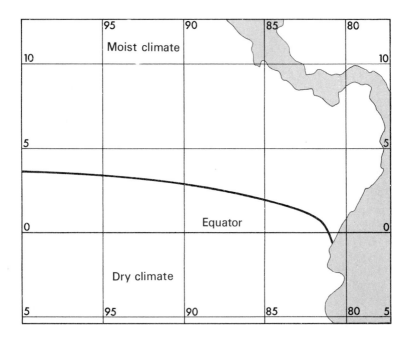

Pacific, at least in its eastern and central part, this dry trade wind zone extends almost to the equator, so that the dry equatorial zone of the Southern Hemisphere is balanced against the moist equatorial zone of the Northern Hemisphere (figure 62). This is why the intertropical convergence zone between the trade winds always lies north of the equator, with a few rare exceptions, and for this reason a south-east trade wind nearly always reaches and crosses the equator. Here the air is generally descending but the generally dry weather is sometimes broken by tropical summer rains accompanying a strong perturbation which moves south across the equator close to the intertropical convergence zone.

In the *equatorial rainy zone* (7) rain falls mostly in the form of heavy showers from isolated towering clouds which sometimes form in temporary convergence lines. But occasionally there are extensive perturbations accompanied by billowing clouds which result in persistent rain; only the strongest of these perturbations become tropical hurricanes. Except in mountainous regions, however, dry weather always returns for several days or weeks. The irregular course of the weather is reflected in the varied amounts of precipitation and in the changing direction of the winds which are mostly quite weak. The temperatures remain uniformly high but have a mean value of 27°C at sea level. The highest temperatures do not exceed 34°C and the lowest do not sink below 20°C.

The water-vapour content also remains uniformly high: at midday the relative humidity scarcely falls below 60%, and at night, dew or ground fog forms quite regularly. Europeans find this sweltering heat of the equatorial lowlands extremely enervating in spite of recent improvements in local living conditions.

Since the temperature decreases slowly with height at the rate of about 1°C for every 200 m, Europeans find it comfortable to live at heights between 1,500–1,800 m, as for instance in Nairobi where temperatures lie between 17–19°C, but find it a little too cold at altitudes between 2,600–3,000 m, as for instance in Quito and Bogota, where temperatures lie between 12–14°C.

Regular diurnal changes in wind direction occur in the mountainous regions and along the sea coast and, as we already know, they are called mountain and valley, land and sea breezes. Locally they may dominate the course of the weather. Over the great mountainous islands of Indonesia of which Borneo alone, with an area of 750,000 km^2, is bigger than France, gigantic cloud banks with extensive crystalline heads form every afternoon and lead to heavy tropical downpours. Yet over the surrounding seas the sky is almost completely clear. When night falls, the direction of the temperature gradient is reversed and the weather becomes fine towards sunrise, apart from a few strands of fog above the steaming forests and rice fields. Over the sea, however, there are tremendous, garishly illuminated mountains of cloud, which produce thundery showers. Here also the amount of rain varies from day to day in accordance with the general weather situation which, however, is difficult to identify on ground weather maps.

These daily processes are so regular that in some places, for instance in the former Buitenzorg in Java, which has thunderstorms on 300 days of the year, life is planned around them. The opposite phenomenon occurs in central Africa over the great Lake Victoria, which has an area of 69,000 km², and the surrounding low hills. The nightly convergence of the weak land breeze over the middle of the lake produces a maximum precipitation of more than 220 cm a year, whereas the precipitation on the banks of the lake amounts to only 80–150 cm a year. In the hollows of the great valleys of the higher mountainous regions the regular divergence of the daytime anabatic or mountain breezes gives reduced amounts of precipitation. Although local wind systems reverse their direction when night falls, (figure 36), the nightly katabatic or valley breezes are appreciably weaker so that rains are rare events in the hollows of a valley.

Over the oceans the equatorial rainy zone lies roughly between 2–8°N and spreads out over the continent as far as Indonesia and into the Southern Hemisphere. It is only in eastern Africa and the Somali peninsula, including the neighbouring sea areas, that there are some breaks in this continuous equatorial rainy zone. These breaks take the form of desert-like strips of aridity caused by the divergence of wind currents which are deflected from their paths by the mountainous regions of Ethiopia and by the coast line.

In some areas of Africa and America, particularly between 0–5°S and 5–10°N, it is possible to identify two rainy and two dry periods, the result of the seasonal migration of the inter-tropical convergence zone. In individual years, however, the beginning of these two rainy and dry periods varies a great deal. In this zone there is a large variation of precipitation from year to year and this is very important to the local economies. The differences are caused by anomalies in the local and regional circulation systems.

In the *tropical summer rain zone* (6), often referred to as the marginal tropics, the weather conditions in the summer in each of the hemispheres are the same as those of the equatorial rainy zone. The rainy season usually begins and ends with impressively heavy thunderstorms during the passage of the intertropical convergence zone. The winter dry period is dominated by dry easterly winds with thick haze reaching to 3–4,000 m. This haze is thickened by smoke from grass and bush fires – fires lit by the local inhabitants towards the end of the dry season in accordance with a centuries-old tradition, apparently to increase the richness of the grass vegetation. The temperature before the beginning of the rainy season is particularly high as the midday sun is very near its zenith. The time lag between the movement of the vertical sun and consequent changes in the atmospheric circulation is almost everywhere about 1–2 months. The midday temperatures in the interior of the continents then rise to 42–46°C, but the night temperatures never fall below 25°C because the haze prevents strong transmission of radiation which in turn prevents the ground from cooling off.

This applies particularly to the Indian monsoon region. In this region heavy precipitation nearly always falls during summer on the west coasts of the upper and lower Indian peninsula and the edge of the Himalayas and also in the north-east of the subcontinent (Bengal, East Pakistan, and Assam). But when the precipitation is too heavy the rivers in the low-lying valleys overflow causing devastating floods. Rain in the rest of the region falls only in association with migrating cyclonic disturbances (monsoon depressions) which travel in a north-westerly direction from the Gulf of Bengal. The paths followed by these monsoon depressions vary greatly and are not infrequently influenced by the troughs of the upper westerly winds passing to the north, whose offshoots over the highlands of Tibet can reach a latitude of about 28°. If, under their influence, these monsoon cyclones move towards the north, great wind divergences occur in other regions of the subcontinent creating periods of great dryness (monsoon pauses).

Careful investigations have shown that the summer rainy period in the north-east of this subcontinent begins in April or May, before there is any seasonal change in the upper wind systems. Yet the change in this region is particularly marked: in the summer, between the middle of June and the beginning of September, a steady tropical easterly jet stream attaining speeds up to 150 km/h blows over a westerly stream of the 'monsoon' about 5·7 km deep, which is the most spectacular part of the equatorial westerly winds. From October to May, on the other hand, we find an easterly to north-easterly stream only 1–2 km deep in the north, but 6–8 km in the south, over which the extra-tropical global westerlies dominate, with a subtropical jet stream between the latitudes 25–30° travelling at even higher speeds. This north-east monsoon corresponds to the trade wind, and is responsible for the dry season in the winter. The south-west monsoon blows over the wide spaces of the tropical Indian Ocean where it gathers water vapour, and is then forced upward by the mountainous west coast of both peninsulas. The summer rainy season is limited here to the period when this wind blows, the rest of the year being almost rainless. A peculiarity of the east coast of the Deccan, and also of the eastern coastal regions of Thailand and the east coast of upper India, is that in late autumn (October till December) tropical cyclones cause heavy precipitation and are responsible for the main rainy period in these areas.

The dryness of the Thar desert and its neighbouring districts of Rajasthan and the former Sind on the banks of the lower Indus is due to the absence of summer rains. The SW monsoon is forced here to split up into several diverging and subsiding streams by the higher temperatures of the chain of mountains surrounding the Indus. The depth of this stream, 1,000–1,500 m, is insufficient, although there is no change in its moisture content, to cause showers, and monsoon depressions here are very rare.

In India there are four different seasons: a relatively cool winter from mid-December to March, when rain falls regularly only in the north-west; an extremely hot, dry period before the monsoon

63 A schematic cross-section through
an intertropical front along a line
joining Karachi and Poona. Although surface
monsoon air lies over the desert, the layer
is rarely deep enough to produce rainfall.

173

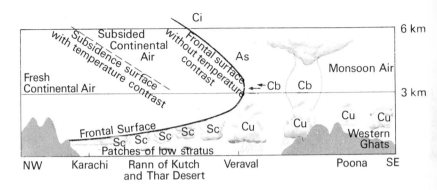

(April and May); a noticeably cooler rainy season of monsoon
(June-September); and a warmer period again during the retreat of
the monsoon accompanied by cyclonic rain on the east coasts.

The summer rains in northern Africa are also limited to the zone
of the south-west monsoon which is 1,000–1,500 m deep on the west
coast but increases to about 2,500 m over the Nile valley. Fully
developed monsoon cyclones hardly ever occur here. Instead more
or less regular wind convergence lines form and travel westward
with the overlying easterly stream causing thunderstorms and
showers which are responsible for most of the rainfall in these
areas. Precipitation reaches its maximum on the western edge of
the mountainous regions of Ethiopia where the lower westerly
winds rise and are diverted northward. In the lee of these
mountainous regions in the Red Sea trough, the Danakii desert,
and the flat eastern part of Ethiopia, the summers are dry although
a little rain falls at the beginning and end of the tropical summer
rainy season.

In the Southern Hemisphere tropical summer rains penetrate
into the heart of the continents, forming southern summer heat
lows in the Gran Chaco, in the Kalahari, and in the Great
Australian desert. Some of the rains regularly reach 22–25°S,
sometimes even 28°, so that a few isolated summer showers always
occur in the dry central zone.

The subtropical dry zone (5) exists in only a few areas in its extreme form where no rain falls at all for years. This applies to the central portions of the Sahara at a latitude of 21–26°N, extending from West Africa to the Red Sea, and above all to the Atacama desert in northern Chile between 20–22°S, where it has not rained for decades. The incoming and outgoing radiation process proceeds almost unhindered, so that the temperature fluctuations between day and night are very great.

At some places the sunshine totals amount to over 90% of the maximum possible, and the few high and medium-high clouds hardly affect the radiation budget at all. The difference between the average daily maximum and minimum temperatures frequently exceeds 20°C and reaches 30°C in areas where the moisture content of the air is low. The dryness of the subsiding air contributes towards this. In summer a deep haze layer forms to a height of 3–4 km above the sandy and dusty areas. This not only reduces the visibility very considerably, the long-wave radiation also reduces the nocturnal cooling of the ground. The high moisture content of air near the sea coasts also does this, particularly around smaller seas such as the Red Sea and the Persian Gulf, where water temperatures in the summer exceed 30°C. But in the winter in regions where the air is of polar origin it is possible for ground frost to occur in the early hours of the morning and for the dew-point to sink frequently to below 0°C.

On the north side of the Sahara in winter and spring irregular precipitation takes place in association with lows in the westerly air stream, whereas on the south side of the desert in summer lows are associated with tropical perturbations in an easterly air stream. Rain occurs for both reasons almost every year in the central, arid, mountainous regions of Hoggar and Tibesti. In all the mountains in the dry zone, local heating regularly produces converging slope or valley winds which, when the atmospheric layering is unstable during the development of depressions and other synoptic perturbations, causes billowing clouds and showers. But the height of cloud base is also relevant. Rain drops from clouds are more

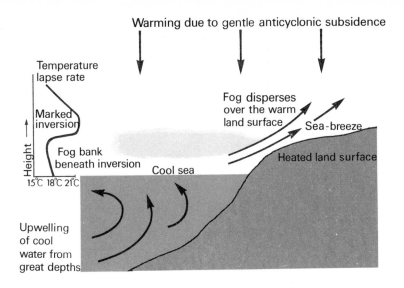

Warming due to gentle anticyclonic subsidence

Temperature lapse rate

Marked inversion

Fog disperses over the warm land surface

Sea-breeze

Height

Fog bank beneath inversion

Cool sea

Heated land surface

15°C 18°C 21°C

Upwelling of cool water from great depths

likely to reach high than low ground without evaporating, particularly in this region. In the Arabian peninsula the rare rainfalls occur exclusively in spring. In the mountainous districts of northern Baluchistan as well as the northern Punjab, winter and summer rains overlap regularly and yield an average annual rainfall of about 50 cm. The rainfall in the Peshawar basin is 4–6 cm a month from January to May, and from July to August, and 1 cm respectively in June, October and November. The figure for the whole year is 30 cm. These areas, therefore, cannot be regarded as belonging to the really arid zones.

Arid areas also exist outside the regions of the subtropical high pressure cells. They are caused either by the divergence of air currents close to the ground or by descending air currents to the lee of mountains. The weather in the grimmest desert in the world, the Atacama desert in north Chile, is due not only to its position in the belt of the subtropical high pressure cells but also to the tropical easterly stream which is forced downward in the lee of the Andes mountains whose average height is 4,000 m.

The trade wind zone of the west coast of the continents includes a particularly interesting group of arid areas. There we find offshore winds and winds parallel to the coastline which set in motion the shallow warm surface layer of the oceans near the coast. To compensate for this, cool deep water at 14°–20°C has to rise to take the place of the warmer tropical surface water at 26°–27°C. This causes the air above to be cooled from below and instead of rain over the sea we merely get a shallow haze and fog banks. Since deep cool water borders on the strongly heated land, an almost constant circulation of air between sea and land is created, lasting throughout the day, and this drives the sea fog landward. In contact with this warmer surface the fog rises and finally dissolves (figure 64). Where these conditions exist, that is, along the coasts of California, Peru, south-west Africa, Angola, Morocco (to a lesser extent), and in the summer also along the coasts of Somaliland and southern Arabia when the winds blow from the south-west, the coastal deserts are characterised by cool adjoining waters and cool local air, and by fog, particularly in summer. This sea fog, moving in towards the hills, frequently results in very fine, penetrating drizzle which helps to produce thick vegetation. Such wet fogs are known as 'Garua' in Peru, and 'Cacimbo' in Angola. In San Francisco they sweep through the 'Golden Gate', with its huge bridge, into the Bay where they quickly dissipate. Their upper boundary is quite low, mostly below 6–800 m. Above it, when the temperatures are high, the weather is fine, so that the inhabitants of San Francisco and Lima have no difficulty in escaping the cold and foggy weather.

The existence of such a low altitude inversion is a prerequisite for the formation of the notorious 'smog' of Los Angeles, whose name is derived from a combination of the words 'smoke' and 'fog.' The gaseous waste combustion products from industry and countless refuse incinerators, and the exhaust fumes from 2 million motor cars rise into this lower layer of the atmosphere which is already naturally hazy. The smog, formed in this way, is then moved backward and forward by the daily alternation of sea and land breezes. The main reason for this phenomenon is that the low lying inversion in the summer prevents any vertical exchange from taking place. The passage of any perturbations, particularly the winter cold fronts, dissipates this inversion at least temporarily and with it the pollution of the air.

The subtropical winter rainy zone (4) is fully developed only along the western parts of the continents. The best known example and the largest in area is the European Mediterranean region where the weather in the summer is almost invariably dry at least south of about 43° latitude. This is because of the offshoots of the high from the Azores. But in the cold season of the year frontal and non-frontal depressions travel with the westerlies of this zone and cause heavy rainfalls which, however, do not last very long. In the northern part of the Mediterranean area, these rains occur mostly in the spring and autumn. In the southern part, around 35°N, they occur exclusively in the months from November to March.

The summer dry period increases from about two months in the north to about eight to nine months along the African coast. During this same period steady northerly winds are observed from Italy and the Adriatic towards Iraq, Iran and Afghanistan. These winds are caused by the strong zonal pressure gradient between the Azores high (about 1,025 mb) and the thermal low in the Persian Gulf and the Punjab (995–1,000 mb). They have been known in Greece and the Aegean since ancient times as 'Etesian winds', which is the reason why the whole subtropical winter rainy zone is often described, somewhat confusingly, as the region of the Etesian climate. Some of these winter and spring rains travel as far as Turkestan and penetrate into the central Asian high mountain range and, as mentioned above, into the Sahara, Arabia, and the Punjab. The weather variations they cause can now be followed on upper-air weather charts from the Atlantic, across Asia Minor and northern India to southern China. Beyond 75° east, however, no summer dry period is observed as a consequence of the Indian monsoon.

Similar seasonal movements and variations in the weather are found in the area of California and Oregon and southern Chile, where the Andes prevent the eastward spread of the winter rains in the region of the Cape in South Africa and along the south-west and south coasts of Australia. The plants and trees in these winter rainy regions have adapted their period of growth and flowering to the prevailing climatic conditions, for intense radiation and high temperature during the summer require strong protective measures to prevent excessive transpiration.

In the temperate zone (3) where the weather is governed all the year round by the westerlies, there are no regular dry periods of any length. This is true of most European countries. The main characteristic of the temperate zone is the constant alternation between short periods of bad weather and anticyclonic fine weather periods lasting several days.

The temperatures in this zone can vary considerably, according to latitude and season. Two typical, but by no means extreme examples, are the mean annual temperature in New Orleans, which is +20°C, and the mean annual temperature in Winnipeg which is +2°C (−19°C in January and +19°C in July).

The prevailing SW and W winds cause surface oceanic currents with nearly the same average direction. The Gulf Stream and its continuations, the North Atlantic Drift in the Atlantic, and the Kuro-shio in the Pacific, carry warm surface waters from tropical latitudes (from the Caribbean Sea and the South China Sea), and rapidly warm even very cold polar air masses from below. The heating of the air above the warm sea surfaces, which occurs regularly in winter off the coast from Maine to Newfoundland and over the Japanese Sea, has been carefully studied and found to be one of the greatest known exchanges of energy, and of vital importance to the weather. According to Japanese research workers, the amount of energy regularly transferred to the atmosphere from the sea amounts to 900–1,200 Ly/day, mainly in the form of latent heat of water-vapour.

The air which leaves the snow-covered continent at temperatures around −30°C is heated at the rate of up to 10°C a day by the warm waters, whose temperatures a small distance offshore can rise to 18°C. During this process, however, the heated air becomes unstable. Turbulent 'Arctic sea smoke', a whispy fog, often forms above the relatively warm waters. After a short time distinctive, low-level cumulus clouds are formed which in some regions, such as the north coast of Japan in winter, give rise to heavy falls of snow almost daily. Snowfalls of 2–3 m are by no means uncommon on low-lying land. Similar conditions are created, though not quite so severely, when in winter masses of cold air begin to blow over the still unfrozen Baltic, Hudson Bay, the Great Lakes of America or the Caspian Sea.

After passing over 1,500–2,000 km of open ocean, the airstreams have acquired the temperature of the sea water to within 1–2°C, but polar air masses remain unstable and colder than the water, whereas tropical air masses are stable and warmer than the water. The interchange of these air masses, and the vertical movements in their boundary zones and fronts, play a major role in the course of the weather in the whole temperate zone.

Occasionally warm high pressure cells transform themselves into 'blocking' anticyclones. This happens particularly often in spring and early summer over the British Isles and the North Sea, and in autumn and winter over Scandinavia and the Baltic Sea. It also happens even more frequently in the sea regions of Alaska but scarcely at all in the Southern Hemisphere.

If we ignore these quasi-stationary high pressure regions for a moment, we see that the waves and whorls of the westerlies nearly always travel from west to east. Waves and whorls, with predominantly maritime air masses, govern the course of the weather on the west coast of the continents including most of the western half of Europe. Where mountains force them to rise, as in northwestern Spain, Wales, the Lake District of England, Scotland, and especially in western Norway, the frequency of precipitation rises to 200–280 days a year, with an annual precipitation of 3–5 m.

At sea level in Norway, say at Bergen, the precipitation amounts to 2 m, but at the end of the Sognefjord, deep inland, this decreases to about 40 cm, and to as little as 28 cm in the Otta valley with its salty soil, which actually requires irrigation.

The air masses, warmed by the North Atlantic Drift, prevent the mean winter temperatures along the coast and on the offshore islands from falling below 0°C, even at a latitude of 70°. If, however, a blocking high causes continental air to spread westward, temperatures fall to −3° to −8°C in Ireland, and on the outermost Norwegian islands. The unusually mild climate of the coastal regions of Europe – in Norway for instance the mean January temperature lies 28°C above the mean for its latitude – is therefore caused not directly, but indirectly, by the Gulf Stream and North Atlantic Drift. The basic cause is the prevailing westerly wind stream which drives the oceanic warm currents.

The deeper we penetrate into the interior of Eurasia the more frequently we find continental air masses from the east which bring with them severe cold in winter and, conversely, high temperatures in summer. This alternation is particularly marked in winter: in European Russia, in the Moscow region for instance, (mean January temperature −10°C), periods of rain with melting snow alternate with icy snowstorms and temperatures below −35°C. Nearly the same also happens in the interior of Siberia where temperatures alternate between a little below 0°C and −50°C, each time under the influence of air masses of different origin.

High pressure periods are still more frequent in May and September in east-central Europe, where a sort of Indian summer is associated with a period of settled weather. North of the Alps and the Carpathians, on the other hand, there are frequent rains from June to August. Early winter is in general rather dull and mild, and particularly cloudy in the transition regions over Poland and White Russia. Areas in which there are anticyclones in the winter are characterised by the occurrence of inversions with persistent fogs.

Very high or very low precipitation figures can occur in any month, but in the Atlantic coastal regions as far north as Norway, totals of precipitation fall predominantly in autumn and winter, whereas in the interior of the continents, and in south-east England the maximum rainfall is in summer. This, however, applies only to the amount of precipitation, as duration and frequency of precipitation is generally less in summer than in winter, except in the northern Alpine foothill regions.

The amount and frequency of precipitation decreases towards the interior of Eurasia: yet the precipitation in Siberia up to the Yenissei is hardly less than that in the European part of Russia. Parts of the subtropical dry zone extend to the Gobi steppes and to 48°N in the shadow of the Altai Mountains. The Tarim basin in east Turkestan, completely surrounded by high mountain ranges, is extremely arid and can be described as the most continental region on earth, its aridity extending even to the north of the Tibetan highlands.

In North America, the extensive and varied Western Cordillera ranges hinder the penetration of maritime air masses into the interior of the continent. For this reason the subtropical dry zone extends from Arizona where, however, showers originating in the Gulf of Mexico occur regularly, to the central parts of the continent and along the eastern side of the Rocky Mountain range to about 54°N. But in these same areas extremely cold air from the Canadian polar regions moves southward without topographic hindrance. Several times every winter this cold air reaches as far as the Gulf coast at temperatures of −10°C or less and, after being heated strongly by the subtropical warm sea, may even reach tropical central America. Temperature fluctuations over central and eastern North America are as great as over eastern Asia, Korea, and Manchuria. It is by no means unusual for the temperature to fall from +15°C to −18°C, or the reverse in 24 hours. Heavy snow falls of up to 50–80 cm a day and catastrophic glazed frosts or ice rains during which supercooled droplets of rain turn into ice on contact with the ground are also not rare during the long and severe winters, not even in the large cities of the eastern United States.

In the summer, tropical air masses from the Gulf of Mexico bring to the southern states like Texas and to the east coast and

Great Lakes region, a moist, sweltering heat which is difficult to bear. Mean summer temperatures in Washington D.C. are +26°C which is close to the mean temperature of the equatorial zone. In winter, on the other hand, cold polar air from the cold centre of the Canadian archipelago gives remarkably low average temperatures in the interior of the continent and along the coast. In Omaha, for instance, the figure is −6°C and in New York −1°C, which is very different from the figure of +8°C for Naples in the Mediterranean, at the same latitude, but similar to the figure of −4°C for Peking.

In Eastern Asia the westerly winds with their frontal depressions predominate all the year round. The so-called south-east monsoon in China and Japan is a wind system only 500–1,000 m deep which has very little influence on the course of the weather. Summer rain comes mostly from the south-west or the south. In summer, warm moist air from the south-west meets cooler air from the north-west over west and central China to the lee of the Tibetan Highlands. A frontal zone there moves northward in June–July and retraces its steps southward in August and September. Its rapidly moving perturbations produce intense summer rains north of the Yangtse-Kiang (about 30°N). In winter, cold air from Siberia usually forces its way towards the south-east across the mountains but is then rapidly transformed. The main frontal zone then lies over southern China and runs south of the main islands of Japan. Its unusual strength and stability is reflected in the greatest surface temperature differences and the highest mean wind velocities in the free atmosphere.

The great westerly winds of the *Southern Hemisphere* travel almost entirely over the seas in latitudes between 40–60° and are strongly maritime in character. Their particular properties are an evenness of seasonal temperature – for instance on Macquarie Island at a latitude of 54° the January temperature is 6·4°C and the July temperature 2·9°C – the almost constant stormy winds, and the extraordinary frequency of depressions, fronts, and precipitation. Seasonal variations of weather are almost as small as

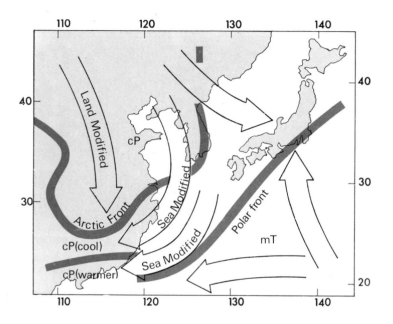

65 Winter air masses and frontal zones over eastern Asia. The strong thermal gradient over southern China is well marked with cold unmodified continental air being in close proximity to the warmer sea-modified air.

at the equator but great variations can take place from year to year as a result of persistent anomalies in the general circulation of the atmosphere.

Contrasts between the windward and the lee sides of the Chilean Andes or the New Zealand Alps are very marked indeed. Precipitation decreases from 4–6 m on the windward side to 30–40 cm on the lee side. Under the protection of the Andes the subtropical dry area of South America reaches its most southerly point near 52°S. Temperatures are noticeably lower than in the Northern Hemisphere, particularly in the Atlantic and Indian Ocean regions where Antarctic ice and cold waters push 5–10°C nearer the equator than in the Pacific regions. Bouvet Island (54°S), for instance, is covered with glaciers almost to the

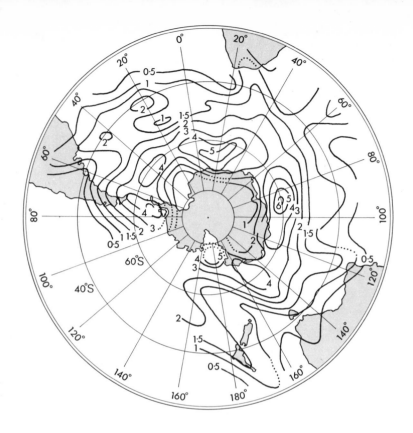

coast whereas, in summer, Heligoland and Sylt in the same latitude in the Northern Hemisphere, are popular bathing resorts.

Three hundred days of rain a year and an average cloud cover of 80–85% are not rare in this inhospitable and stormy sea area. On Heard Island (53°S, 23°E) sunshine totals are only 12% of the maximum possible and precipitation falls nearly 30% of the time. The presence of an extensive inland ice region, over 200 km long, in Patagonia (48–9°S) is a further example of the harsh climates in the Southern Hemisphere.

Antarctic waters with temperatures below 2°C in winter and 5°C in summer, meet warmer waters from the north in an oceanic

66 Frequency of depressions in the Southern Hemisphere based on a sample from January to February 1947, mid March to mid April 1947, and mid March to mid April 1948.

185

convergence with a temperature rise of several degrees. This occurrence, which affects weather, occurs in latitudes 48–50°S in the Indian and Atlantic sectors but in latitudes 54–62° in the Pacific. These considerable differences in latitude are obviously related to the shape of the Antarctic continent.

In the Northern Hemisphere the area of the oceanic *subpolar zone* (2) is also one of the most inhospitable regions of the world. Storms from varying directions occur there very frequently. Clouds are thick, and on 250–300 days a year rain, snow and sleet fall in quick succession, while in all seasons temperatures fluctuate under the influence of polar cold waves and surges of warm air. In Iceland and southern Greenland, the low summer temperatures of 10–11°C and strong winds make it possible for only dwarf birches to grow, and then only in sheltered locations: there are no high trees.

Inland ice sheets and glaciers occur in the higher mountain areas from about 60°N, for instance in southern Iceland, Norway, and southern Alaska. But in the shelter of the mountains, towards the interior of these countries, the climate by contrast becomes characterised by greatly contrasting seasonal values. The summers are short with intense insolation but the weather changes frequently and there is heavy precipitation. In Swedish Lapland, in interior Alaska, and even at the Siberian cold pole (Verkhoyansk), all at a latitude of about 68°N, the maximum temperature is +37°C, which is as high as in northern Germany or Denmark. The winter snow cover lasts 7–9 months and often reaches a depth of 80–100 cm by the beginning of spring. Subarctic bushes such as birches and willows grow below the surface of the snow cover, which protect them from the icy winter storms.

The ground remains frozen for still longer periods, and in many parts of the continental subarctic zone there are areas in which the ground thaws to a depth of only 150 cm in summer. In the centre of the subarctic, in eastern Siberia when there is little snow, the depth of the frozen ground or permafrost exceeds 600 m. This frozen ground prevents the absorption of snow-melt in summer and so almost impassable swamps and bogs are formed. All

67 The present distribution
of the permafrost zone in
the Northern Hemisphere.

houses, railway lines, roads, and airfields require special precautions against the effect of thawing, or frost-heaving, which is a
very costly matter. The zone of permafrost stretches from both
sides of Hudson Bay to about 56°N, and in eastern Siberia to
nearly 50°N. Both lie in the cold air region of lows which are
constantly forming over eastern North America and Asia.

Winter minimum temperatures over the snow cover regularly
sink to below −40°C, but hardly ever below −60°C. The exception
is in eastern Siberia, in the region of Lena and in the adjoining
mountain basin where temperature minima of −70°C and even
−78°C have been recorded, with a monthly mean of −48°C. These
were the figures for Ojmjakon at 60°N, 140°E. This zone is hardly
affected by migrating depressions which confine themselves either
to the Arctic Ocean region or else travel east-south-east from
central Siberia across Mongolia to northern China. In winter there
is fine radiation weather with no wind, which is uncommon elsewhere in that climatic zone. In the same zone, summer temperatures are sufficiently great to produce forests of tall trees which, in
spite of the long-lasting winter snow cover, reach far across the
polar circle to the Taimyr peninsula (71°N). Lake Baikal, which
has an area of 31,000 km² and is 1,500 m deep, produces an
extraordinary local climate, for although it is surrounded by the
severe cold of the Siberian winter, it remains ice-free until the end
of December and then freezes until June. In summer, its temperature is 10°C cooler and in the early winter months, 14°C warmer than
the temperature of its continental surroundings.

In the Southern Hemisphere the 'subantarctic zone' is stormier
and very much colder than the oceanic regions of the Northern
Hemisphere. This is the main area for hunting whales in summer,
during which the weather is very changeable. It is also subject to
great variations from year to year, particularly in the neighbourhood of the pack-ice boundary. The huge flat icebergs broken off
from the Antarctic shelf, some the size of Belgium, melt only
slowly and are therefore seen only in exceptional circumstances in
lower latitudes. Predominantly easterly and frequently stormy

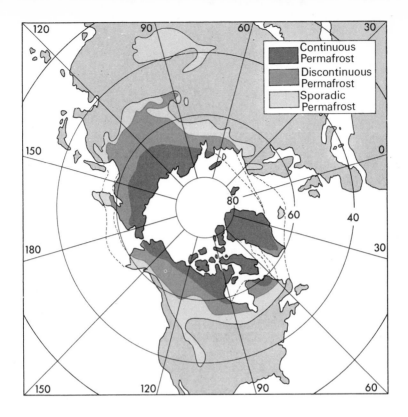

winds blow close to the Antarctic coast. The courses of the cyclones are subject to considerable variation but, contrary to what occurs in the Northern Hemisphere, the circulation is predominantly zonal; blocking high pressure areas and the weather conditions associated with them are exceptional. The reason for the weak meridional exchange must be the absence of any great land masses in the area between 45 and 70°S. Temperature differences along parallels of latitude are much smaller in the Southern Hemisphere than those in the Northern Hemisphere, the circulation is predominantly zonal; mid-January temperature is +3°C on the Lofoten Islands and −47°C at Verkhoyansk. This difference is about as great as that between the equator and the pole!

The high polar climatic zone (1) differs from the subpolar zone mainly in a smaller frequency of depressions and appreciably lower winter temperatures. Long periods of fine weather are common only in spring and are associated with relatively warm anticyclones. The visibility in this air, which is free from dust and contains little water-vapour, is exceptionally good. Colours are strikingly vivid and contrasts between light and shade are very strong because of the low elevation of the sun. Twilight and the aurora borealis offer magnificent and unforgettable spectacles.

The Arctic Ocean is covered by an ice layer made up of countless ice floes, the majority of which are only about 250 cm thick. Below this ice layer which, in September, covers 10 million km² and in March and April 18 million km², the ocean loses its heat only slowly and its temperature never sinks below −2°C, the freezing point of salt water, while the air temperature rarely falls below about −40°C. Winter mean temperatures generally lie only a little below −30°C. It takes a long time in spring before the snow cover on the ice begins to melt. The surfaces of the ice floes themselves melt from the end of June to the beginning of September and gaps form between individual floes. This process uses up so much latent heat that the temperature never rises appreciably above freezing point. A shallow high-lying fog indicates the presence of a permanent inversion of temperature since the melting process constantly removes heat from the lower layers of warmer air reaching these areas.

In Greenland, frequent cyclonic precipitation maintains the inland ice sheet which covers nearly 2 million km² of the country, and in particular the southern part which rises to about 2,700 m. North Greenland is dry and is the only example of a cold desert. It consists of bare rocks stretching over 200 km and temperatures may reach as much as 18°C, during 22 hours of sunlight a day in the summer at a latitude of 81°. At the ice cap, however, the air, with its low temperature maintained by the high surface reflection of radiation, is drawn by the force of gravity along the surface of the ice and emerges from the valleys in the form of violent Föhn-like winds. The intense summer insolation has hardly any thermal effect because 80–85% of it is reflected back again. In spite of this, the inland mass of ice in Greenland, contrary to popular opinion, is not the main cold source in the Northern Hemisphere. The main cold source lies over the Canadian archipelago, particularly above the inland ice-caps of Baffin Land and Ellesmere Island. The summer thaw period is very short there, and temperatures in the troposphere, particularly in summer, are almost always the lowest to be found in the Northern Hemisphere.

The most intense of the cold centres, however, is that above the Antarctic where the inland ice sheet reaches altitudes of 4,000 m, an average thickness of 2,200 metres and covers about 13 million km², which is equivalent to 1½ times the area of Europe up to the Urals, and about 7 times the area of the Greenland ice. But in contrast to what occurs in Greenland, the Antarctic surface rarely thaws, for the reflectivity of its snow cover is as high as 85–90%. In spite of the intense insolation in summer, temperatures in the interior of the Antarctic never rise above −20°C and at points on the coast not above 0°C. In winter no heat is available from below as it is in the Arctic Ocean, and temperatures in the interior of these regions sink regularly to below −70°C; even −88°C has been recorded on several occasions by the Russian weather stations at Vostok and Sovietskaia.

If we look at the temperatures of the troposphere as a whole, we find that the average temperatures over the South Pole in summer are only a few degrees higher than those over the North Pole in winter. Over the year we find that the temperature in the Antarctic troposphere is always about 11°C below that in the troposphere above the North Pole. This difference is due mainly to differences in the heat budget, in spite of the fact that similar amounts of incoming solar radiation are involved, and also to the smaller meridional exchange that takes place over the sea areas of the Southern Hemisphere. The inland ice of both Greenland and the Antarctic is fed by snowfalls caused by migrating depressions. Even in the interior of the Antarctic, the snow cover deepens by about 5 cm a year and the average for the whole continent is 15 cm.

Although we have now considered very briefly all the most important climatic types and their genetic relationship within the general atmospheric circulation, we still have to examine some of the basic principles of the boundary definition of climatic zones. There is a confusing divergence of opinion among experts. Many scientists prefer to define the boundaries of these zones in a subjective rather than an objective manner. This method has its advantages if one is considering or teaching the subject of climate in general terms. It necessarily fails, however, when applied to a particular area and when climatic regions are represented on large scale maps, for instance a scale of 1:1 million. This applies also to all the genetic classifications we have considered which are meaningful at the most on 1:50 million maps. But practical climatology maps with a scale up to 1:50,000 require precise quantitative information on these particular regions and districts.

The representation of climate on large-scale maps has been called 'Topoclimatology' by Thornthwaite and 'Terrain Climatology' by Knoch; it is a science which is still in the early stages of its development. Its importance in planning, in selecting for instance the location of a sanatorium, or an atomic reactor, or an orchard or vineyard, can hardly be overestimated.

Within the context of this book we have had to limit ourselves to broad boundary demarcation involving large areas and to a few examples of basic importance. But it is not a practical proposition to use an 'effective' classification, that is, a classification based on the effect a climate has on a particular phenomenon, vegetation for instance, for general purposes. We can of course refer to the ecological effect of climate on the natural vegetation including crops grown by farmers, and to a certain degree also take the water budget of the earth's surface into consideration. The absolute frost boundary plays a very important role here. Tropical plants, for instance, die when their leaf temperature sinks to below 0°C for a few hours and their cellular fluid freezes. Even a short-lived frost every 20–30 years prevents the growth of tropical trees and plants. It is very difficult to determine this absolute frost boundary accurately, for the local distribution of temperature minima is very complicated. Due to the large variability of temperature it is also unsafe to use any other threshold concept, for instance, a temperature below +18°C during the coldest month. The absolute snowfall boundary is not always identical with the absolute frost boundary because snow can fall at air temperatures above 0°C, and frost often occurs in dry climates which are rich in radiation.

In the tropical mountains, frosts can occur above 2,200 m and even 1,800 m in extreme cases so that typical tropical plants like tea, coffee, cocoa, and banana, cannot be cultivated above these heights. In these areas, therefore, such as those of the south and central American Cordilleras and Ethiopia, there are a series of climatic steps which are represented in table 9. It should be strongly emphasised here that outside the tropics the mean annual temperature cannot be taken as the basis for classification. This applies also to any classification on the basis of a relationship between the temperatures of the tropical highland climates and those of the low-lying climates in the higher latitudes, such as has often been attempted by the followers of A. v. Humboldt, since this leads to fundamental misconceptions at least so far as ecology is concerned. The general absence of seasonal variations in temperature in the tropics is the fundamental difference between tropical upland climates and those in other high latitudes.

The natural tree line boundary in the subpolar zone and in mountains is also a temperature boundary along which the mean temperature during the warmest month of the year is 10–11°C. Such a boundary also exists for other plants. Beyond it, lack of sufficient heat prevents growth, or at least, reproduction.

Even more important for the classification of climate is the relationship between precipitation and evaporation. We say a climate is *humid* when precipitation is greater than potential evaporation, and *arid* when the potential evaporation is greater than precipitation. If these conditions obtain every month of the year then we speak of a humid or arid climate. If, however, there is an alternation of humid and arid seasons and months, we speak

Table 8 Selected date from the seven climatic zones *

| Zone and location | Latitude | Longitude | Mean temperature (°C) | |
			Warmest month	Coldest month
1 Cape Chelyuskin	77·7°N	104°E	1·5 Jl.	−28·0 M
2 Reykjavik	64·1°N	22°W	11·2 Jl.	−0·4 Ja
3 Valentia (Eire)	51·9°N	10°W	15·4 Au	6·8 F
4 Lisbon	38·7°N	9°W	22·5 Au	10·8 Ja
5 Alice Springs	23·8°S	134°E	28·2 Ja	11·9 Jl
6 Darwin	12·5°S	131°E	29·2 N	25·1 Jl
7 Singapore	1·3°N	104°E	28·0 Ju	26·1 Ja

Abbreviations of the months :
Ja, F, M, A, My, Ju, Jl, Au, S, O, N, D.

of *semi-humid* or *semi-arid* climates. Although the mean annual and monthly distribution of precipitation is well known, that of potential evaporation is not and attempts are constantly being made to obtain at least approximate figures for it, since it is of such great practical importance. These figures are usually obtained from empirically derived formulae, of which those by C. W. Thornthwaite and H. L. Penman are perhaps the best known. The German geographer Lauer showed in 1952 that typical tropical vegetation – rain forests, various types of savannah, steppes, desert steppes and deserts – quite clearly depended on the duration of the humid or arid seasons. Unfortunately, however, this no longer applies when the average sinks to below freezing point.

The basic aim of all these experiments is essentially to determine the amount of potential evaporation or evapotranspiration, and to relate the figure obtained to precipitation. The real or actual evaporation depends largely on the amount of water that is made

| Mean precipitation (cm) | | Total annual rainfall | Frequency (days) |
Wettest month	Driest month		
3 X	1 W	24	No data
10 O	4 My Ju	80	191
17 D	7 Ap	140	252
11 Ja M	0·3 Jl	71	116
7 DF	1 X	25	32
34 JaF	0·1 Jl	156	98
28 Ja	12 S	228	175

X = several months   W = several winter months
* See Table 7.

available from ground water or precipitation and is therefore not of decisive importance in the classification of climate. The Russian meteorologist M. I. Budyko has suggested a method of classifying climates based on the evaporation-precipitation balance. He argues that since it is possible to measure, or at least estimate accurately, the energy made available from the radiation balance of the earth's surface, there is a relationship between this radiation balance and the energy that is required to evaporate the precipitation that has reached the ground. Such a clear quantitive relationship is reflected quite accurately by the distribution of the different types of vegetation in the vast territory of the Soviet Union. Indeed, this does seem to open up a new approach to the problem of the classification of climate based on sound physical principles within the framework of the water balance. It would be a most valuable consequence if the problem of defining the boundaries of arid climates were solved by this approach.

6 Climatic variations

6 Climatic variations

Is our climate really constant or does it change with time? This is a question which is frequently asked, when weather conditions suddenly become extreme, as they did during the hard winter of 1962–3, when Lake Constance froze up completely for the first time since 1829–30 and snow drifts in the British Isles caused great traffic chaos; or, when the unusually warm dry summer of 1959 produced the 'wine of the century', of highest quality and in great abundance, in the northernmost vineyard areas of the Rhine and Moselle. The years 1959–63 saw a rapid rise of water level in all the lakes of central Africa, from Lake Nyassa and the lakes of the Ethiopian rift valley to Lake Chad which in 1959, for the first time for 80 years, drained water towards the Sahara in the north-east. The great Lake Victoria rose by no less than $2\frac{1}{2}$ m from the end of 1961 to the middle of 1964, reaching its highest level since reliable observations were begun in 1895 (figure 68). The Nile flood in the autumn of 1964 was the severest since 1900. It is not surprising that such unusual events repeatedly make the subject of climatic variations of greater public interest than the slow and unseen processes which are brought to light only after lengthy and difficult investigations involving large areas and long periods of time.

If we plot the course of any continuously observable parameter of the atmosphere, such as temperature, and at the same time disregard the recurrent effect of the rotation of the earth about its own axis and its revolution round the sun, we obtain a graph showing irregular fluctuations (figure 69). This applies equally to the turbulent wind oscillations recorded with the help of sensitive instruments using a time scale of seconds or minutes, the daily and annual fluctuations of mean temperatures, and to the temperatures indicated in deep water deposits by the use of isotope techniques at a time scale of 10^3 to 10^5 years.

There is therefore a whole spectrum of atmospheric turbulence phenomena analogous with the optical spectrum and electro-magnetic waves. The fluctuations of the type shown in figure 69 lead repeatedly to a search for long period trends which may be useful in

68 *Top* Variations in level of Lake Victoria (*top graph*), with heights above local O.D. in metres, and relative frequency of sun spots (*bottom graph*) from 1900 to 1965.
69 *Bottom* Mean monthly temperature variations in lowland Lancashire, England, from 1751 to 1948. The lines represent ten-year running means.

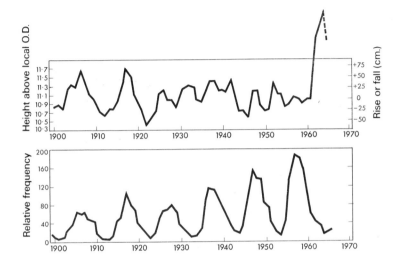

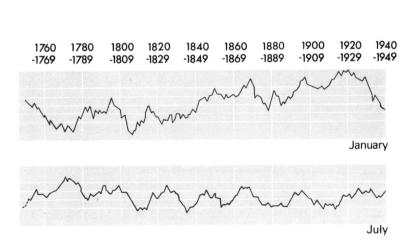

January

July

long-range forecasting, but the search for regular fluctuations with the help of statistical techniques and modern computors has met with very little success. It is true to say, however, that there is hardly a single period from 2 days to 100 years for which one could not find a historical counterpart. Napier Shaw's *Manual of Meteorology* gives numerous series of fluctuations, but these fluctuations are seldom stable in time, nor do they cover a sufficiently large area. In fact, apart from the daily and annual variations hardly any statistically significant periodicity can be said to exist.

Among the exceptions, however, there are two which will be discussed here. These are the periods of sun-spot activity and the 2·2 year period, which has recently attracted attention and which agrees with an as yet unexplained phenomenon in the equatorial stratosphere discovered as recently as 1959. This is a system consisting of sets of 2–3 rings of alternating easterly and westerly winds of great consistency lying above one another and circling the earth. Independently of the geographical longitude they descend at a rate of about 1 km a month, disappearing shortly above the tropopause (100 mb or 16·5 km). At a certain height this process follows a regular 26-month cycle.

The many research workers who have endeavoured to find a correlation between the average 11·2 yearly sunspot activity cycle and meteorological data have obtained surprisingly poor results the moment they tested their finds statistically. A good example is the fluctuation in the height of the water level of Lake Victoria which until about 1922 seemed to be related very closely to the number of sun spots (figure 68), but then underwent variations which were completely independent of them. However, the search for other cycles appears to have been somewhat more successful. There is, for instance, a 5·6 yearly half-period, and especially a 22 year double cycle which, according to H.C.Willett, occurs within the pattern of the general circulation of the atmosphere, and involves, among other things, the frequency in incidence of blocking anticyclones over Europe (figure 70). The latter is a physical reality of the sun, since the polarity of the magnetic field

70 Annual frequency of blocking anticyclones in the zone 10°W to 30°E from 1881 to 1963. (Dots = individual years; line = ten-year running mean).

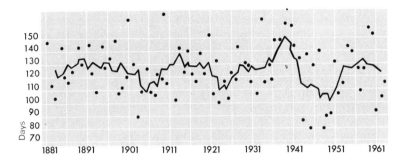

of sun spots changes at the beginning of each new period of sun spot activity. We still know far too little about the reason of such a solar-terrestrial relationship, but presumably the ionosphere and possibly the high ozone content of the air close to the stratopause are related to it. We must, however, look at these cycles critically and not overestimate their importance, for in general the acyclic processes in the troposphere are much more powerful and effective than the cyclic processes, with the exception of the diurnal and annual cycles.

Within this spectrum of atmospheric turbulence phenomena, whose time scale extends over sixteen orders of magnitude ranging from one-tenth of a second to geological time periods of 100 million years, we can most easily deal with climatic fluctuations covering decades or, preferably, centuries. Much longer cycles are of course the only true guide to the whole history of climate and past and present occurrences in the atmosphere of our world. Cycles of this length could, until recent years, be determined only indirectly but the development of isotope analysis has now enabled us to obtain at least some of this information directly.

Meteorological data obtained with the help of instruments exist only since the time of Galileo, a time which also saw the birth of modern physics. But the genuine documented history of climate in Europe did not begin until the Accademia del Cimento in Florence in

1652 and the Royal Society in London, 1660, created a network of weather observation stations. Strictly comparable results, however, were not obtained and published until the Societas Meteorologica Palatina in Mannheim, Germany (1781–95) realised its network extending to Greenland and to North America.

The first network of weather stations promoted and financed by a government was in the small German state of Sachsen-Weimer. Johann Wolfgang von Goethe, whose name we have already mentioned in connection with the classification of clouds, was the minister responsible for this. Unfortunately, however, shortly after his withdrawal from the government, financial difficulties forced the dissolution of the organisation he had created.

The first measurements of rainfall were made in Korea in 1442, although references to rainfall records had already been made in the Old Testament. Regular daily weather records began to be made in the 16th and early 17th century by astronomers of the calibre of Tycho de Brahe and Johannes Kepler. The series of observations made by Haller, the Keeper of the Public Records of Zurich (1546–76), and the Landgrave Hermann IV of Hessen (1623–49) who, as a pupil of Galileo, was an enthusiastic astronomer, give very interesting data concerning climatic fluctuations in the 16th and 17th century. Records of recurrent phenomena like the high water period of the Nile and the summer floods of the Hwang-Ho are also of great value in our study of climatic cycles. So is the information provided by the quality and the quantity of the grape harvest in western Germany, and by the number of rings on the cross-section of tree trunks. Indeed, information on climatic cycles whether accurate or not is available from a great number of sources over the last few thousand years. Examined carefully, historical records are also a good source of information on the history of climate, while records of geological and biological data yield valuable information on its primeval history.

When we look at all the data available from the time measurements were first made with instruments, there is a plethora of

71 Ten-year running means of
precipitation at stations in
NE Brazil (3–5°S, 38–40°W).

201

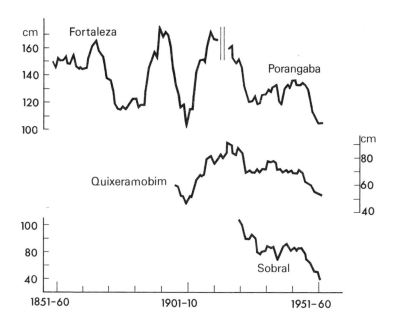

information. A. Wagner, R. Scherhag, C. E. P. Brooks, G. Manley,
H. H. Lamb, and J. Mitchell Jr. have all studied this information
very carefully and obtained some interesting results. We can only
mention a few particularly outstanding examples such as the
surprising temperature variations in Britain (figure 69) and the
marked fall in the frequency of precipitation in the arid areas of
NE Brazil (figure 71). But perhaps the most impressive result is the
revelation of the global rise in temperature from 1880 until about
1945. This rise was hardly noticeable beyond a latitude of 45° in
the Southern Hemisphere, but was more marked in the Atlantic
portion of the Arctic, where rather unusual changes took place in
the area of Greenland and Spitzbergen in the years from 1900 to
about 1945 (figure 72).

72 Temperature fluctuations
for latitudinal zones.
Five-year annual mean departures
from mean 1901 to 1930.

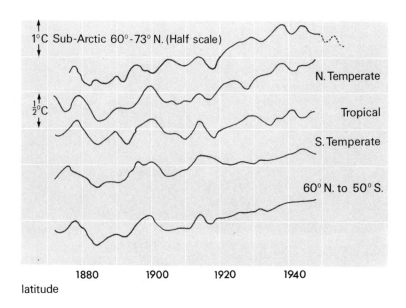

1°C Sub-Arctic 60°-73° N. (Half scale)

N. Temperate

½°C

Tropical

S. Temperate

60° N. to 50° S.

1880   1900   1920   1940

latitude

Many climatic variations are regional in nature. An excess of heat or precipitation in one region is often related to a corresponding deficiency in a neighbouring region. Closer examination, however, reveals a connection between this and the large-scale anomalies in the circulation of the atmosphere that occur so often. If we look at the examples we have been discussing we see that the warm, dry summer of 1959 in north-west and central Europe occurred at the same time as unusually cool weather and heavy precipitation in Russia and western Siberia. A persistent high-level trough over the Urals was responsible for this and its effect extended as far as the area of the Indian summer monsoon. A high pressure ridge of warm air lay over Europe and this steered cold air southward along its eastern flank. The cold winter of 1962–3 was related to a persistent high altitude low over eastern Europe, which led to heavy rain in Italy and North Africa while the east Siberian cold centre shifted westward, and eastern Asia enjoyed a relatively mild winter. Taken over a hemisphere or over the whole globe the anomalies occurring in individual months yield an overall impression of world-wide balance. At the same time they serve as models of climatic changes covering decades and centuries. A study of the geographic distribution of these anomalies reveals their relationship with temperature, pressure, precipitation, and wind. An often quoted example of this is the north Atlantic heat seesaw. When the low pressure areas around Iceland are more intense than usual, southerly winds feed warm air to their eastern part over western Europe and Scandinavia, while northerly winds feed cold air to their western part over Labrador and along the American coastline. The reverse often occurs in both these regions during very cold winter months. Unfortunately, we know very little about the origin of these anomalies in the circulation of the atmosphere but we will return later to this fundamental problem.

In some areas these regional climatic variations have extraordinary consequences. Time and again attempts have been made after a short series of rainy years to grow agricultural produce or raise cattle in the boundary zones of arid districts. There have been examples of this in mid-western North America, in central Asia (Kazakhstan), in north-east Brazil, and in South Africa. But these rainy periods were invariably followed by years of drought, with often catastrophic results. The biological and economic importance of climatic variations can hardly be overestimated in these boundary zones. This applies particularly to the European section of the Arctic. Strong heating in the years between 1900–45 forced the ice boundary back several hundred kilometres. Huge shoals of fish moved northward and higher animals and flowers began to appear. The way of life in Greenland changed: instead of hunters, Eskimos became fishermen, and sheep farming began in the south. The shipping season in Spitzbergen lengthened from three to almost seven months, and it was even possible in summer for ships regularly to take the famous route round Asia eastward

73 Departures of mean temperature for summer (June-August) and winter (December–February) from the 1912–30 average (five-year mean departures) at Isfjord Radio, Spitsbergen.

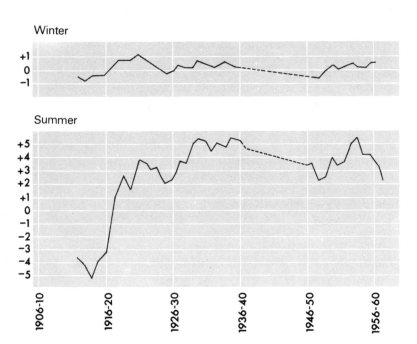

to the mouths of the rivers Ob and Yenisei and westward to the mouth of the Lena. The climate in several regions of northern Russia, northern Siberia and Alaska also improved during this period, which is now apparently coming to an end. At any rate, the ice on the polar sea is now moving forward (south) again in several places, particularly in the region of the east Greenland current and there has been a pronounced deterioration in latter years in the climate of the Arctic.

Regional climatic variations of this type which are the consequence of long persisting anomalies in the circulation of the atmosphere are more frequent and impressive than the less obvious global variations. They essentially involve new distributions of heat or precipitation without affecting mean global physical values. The average temperature on earth, the overall evaporation, and therefore also the overall total precipitation, are exclusively the function of the radiation budget. As long as the amount of radiation from the sun, the solar constant, remains really constant, together with the other physical parameters of the atmosphere, such as the amount of moisture, carbon dioxide, ozone, and haze particles, the mean global values of the meteorological elements will remain exactly unaltered. The law of conservation of mass requires that the average pressure of the atmosphere at the surface of the earth (as opposed to the pressure reduced to sea level) remains constant.

One of the most important discoveries of the last decade has been that these global values are, in fact, not absolutely constant. Finding the reasons for the slight variations that take place with time is one of the most interesting problems in geophysics today. But let us first examine the facts: careful examination of all available data shows that in the years from about 1880–1941 the average temperature of the atmosphere and also that of the surface water of the oceans has risen continuously by about 0·7°C, that is about 0·01°C a year. In the same period, the average rise in the level of the seas was about 1·2 mm a year. Both figures seem insignificant, but over this century they would amount to an increase in global temperature of 1°C and a rise in the level of the sea of 12 cm, which is certainly very remarkable. The hypothetical situation in 1,000 years is alarming and forces us to study these problems with great care.

The world-wide shrinkage of mountain glaciers, apart from those in a few districts in the north-west of the North American continent which are actually increasing, is generally attributed to this increase in temperature. Investigations have shown that the physical processes involved are much more complicated than it was at first thought. If we estimate the amount of water resulting from the melting of glaciers in one year we obtain figures which are comparable to those obtained for the rise of sea level. But the land-locked mountain glaciers represent less than 1 % of the total amount of ice on the surface of the earth. The Antarctic ice-cap, which is on average 2,200 m thick, represents more than 90 % of the volume of ice on our globe, and the Greenland ice about 9 %. Observations and calculations show that the amount of ice in Greenland remains constant, while the ice in the Antarctic is increasing. This brings us to a problem much discussed today, namely, the world water balance. If we assume that the amounts of water gained from or lost to space and generated from the interior of the earth – the so-called 'juvenile' water of volcanoes – are negligibly small, then the total amount of water available on earth is the sum of the water-vapour in the air, the water in the seas, rivers and lakes, and the water in the form of snow and ice on the surface of the earth. And this amount, of course, is constant.

As we saw in an earlier chapter, if all the moisture in the air were condensed to liquid water it would cover the earth to a height of 2·4 cm (or about 1 in) compared with the average sea depth of 3,700 m, whereas if all the ice on land were melted, it would raise the level of the sea by about 75 m. (The ice floating in the polar sea and the Antarctic shelf is disregarded as it is in stable equilibrium with the water).

If the mass of ice in the Antarctic and Greenland increases by 3 cm a year, which is not an unrealistic figure, this must necessarily produce a corresponding 'eustatic' decrease in the level of the seas in the world by about 1 mm a year. But in actual fact there is a rise in level of about this amount. This is probably because the oceans are heated to great depths, and also because the temperature of the air was, until recently, increasing by 0·01°C a year, as mentioned before. The heating results in a decrease in density and so to an increase in the volume of the oceans without any alteration in the mass of the water in the seas.

The obvious question that immediately springs to mind is, of course, to what extent is the amount of insolation, the solar constant, really constant? This question is all the more pertinent because we know that during sun-spot activity the energy produced by the sun in the ultra-violet, x-ray, and gamma-ray part of the spectrum is subject to variation by a factor of up to 1,000! But the energy associated with those parts of the spectrum is only a minute fraction (about 10^{-5}) of the total amount of energy received from the sun. Many attempts have been made to determine whether there is any variation in the amount of energy produced in the visible part of the spectrum, which is the region of maximum energy. Work carried out by the Smithsonian Institute in special high altitude mountain observatories suggested that there had been a slight increase in the value of the solar constant in the period between the two world wars. But sources of error are still much too great, particularly as observations made from the ground cannot exclude the effect of the fluctuating opacity and transparency to radiation of the stratosphere. It will be the role of astronomical satellites to provide reliable figures for the solar constant and the extent, if any, of its variation.

Volcanic eruptions which fling dust particles into the air, eventually reaching into the stratosphere, exert a great influence on the transparency of the upper atmosphere to radiation. The dust manifests its presence in the air in various ways. The gigantic eruptions of the Tambora volcano on the Island of Sumbawa in Indonesia in 1815, of the volcano Krakatau also in Indonesia in 1883, and of the volcano Katmai in Alaska in 1912, hurled several cubic kilometres of matter into the air. The dust clouds following the Krakatau eruption reached a height of at least 32 km, and probably 40 km and beautiful multicoloured twilight effects were observed for 3–4 years after the eruption. The relatively smaller eruption of the Hekla volcano in Iceland in 1947 produced a dust cloud which rose to a height of 28 km.

The rate of fall of particles with a diameter of less than 1 micron is very small, while particles of a diameter below 0·1 micron remain in a state of suspension for an almost unlimited period of time. The interchange of air between the troposphere and stratosphere occurs largely through horizontal transfers in the region of the jet streams and involves mainly the lower part of the stratosphere, whose total mass is replaced every 1–2 years by tropospheric air. With the help of the radioactive isotopes produced by nuclear explosions, the period dust particles spend in the upper stratosphere has been estimated with some accuracy as being between 5 and 10 years. The result of this pollution of the stratosphere by the dust particles from volcanic action is an absorption of about 10 % of the direct radiation from the sun (S). However, half of this amount is transmitted to the earth's surface as sky radiation (H). Nevertheless, an overall reduction in radiation by about 5 % has a marked effect.

The much smaller eruption of the volcano Agung on the Island of Bali in Indonesia in 1963 also injected volcanic dust into the stratosphere. The resulting deep red glowing dust clouds made their appearance first in the Southern Hemisphere and then in the tropics in the autumn of 1963, and in Europe during the following winter. The height of these clouds in the tropics was estimated from aircraft to have been 25–32 km. This was the first time since 1912 that an increase in the opacity of the stratosphere had been observed and measured as the result of a volcanic eruption. The effect, in general, is at least partly responsible for the observed short-time climatic variations. It is a remarkable fact that during the years immediately following each of the great eruptions we have just mentioned, there was a world-wide decrease in temperature, but variable in its distribution. This also occurred in the years following the great volcanic eruptions in Iceland in 1784–6 and in Japan in 1783, after which dust in the stratosphere roused considerable attention in Europe as 'upper air smoke'. But the decrease in temperature in the last one or two decades had already begun before the eruption of Agung which can therefore be held only partly responsible, if at all.

Thanks to the interpretation of much indirect data on climate and also to the utilisation of new and accurate techniques including measurements with isotopes, we are now able to delve much more deeply and further back than previously into the history of climatic variations. This is a development which will continue.

Written records are reasonably easy to interpret, for instance records of the blockading of Iceland by ice, the freezing up and the thawing of the great lakes and rivers of Scandinavia or those in Japan, the height of the Nile floods, and the month when the cherry trees were in blossom in Japan. Inland seas, like the Dead Sea, where the level of the water varies between 10 and 15 m, give valuable information on the water balance of their catchment, that is, precipitation minus evaporation and percolation. The link between this and meteorological data is obvious, although the analysis is not as easy as it might at first appear. This is even more true of information on local floods or cold or hot summers, which is largely subjective, as are statements on the quality and the quantity of the grape harvest near the northern limit of vineyards along the Rhine and the Moselle. Although, of course, there is a statistical relationship between the quality, which essentially means the sugar contents, of the grape, and the summer temperature, or more correctly, the amount of radiation, such things as isolated late frosts, excessive rainfall, pests, or plant diseases, can introduce considerable margins of error.

These objections also apply to the interpretation of tree rings. But thorough studies are currently in progress in the tree ring laboratory in Tucson, Arizona, which will almost certainly yield valuable results. Near the margin of arid regions the thickness of the annual tree rings mainly depends on precipitation; near the latitudinal and altitudinal tree line it depends on summer temperatures; in other regions, on a complicated correlation with a variety of meteorological data.

In Europe and elsewhere, the results of the study of fossilised pollen, coupled with the method of C_{14} (radio-active carbon) dating, have laid a sound foundation for the history of the climate during the whole of the post-glacial period of the last 15,000 years. From our point of view it is interesting to note that the systematic determination of the C_{14} content of tree rings has shown that the production of C_{14} in the upper atmosphere by cosmic radiation is not constant, and has, in fact, been subject to a variation of $\pm 2\%$ in the last 1,200 years. This obviously suggests a possible inaccuracy in the time scale.

A great deal of information, mostly literary, is available, for the climate of the last 1,000 to 1,200 years. On the basis of this it has, for instance, been firmly established that the weather was extraordinarily good in Europe during the period AD 800–1200. The vegetation and glacier boundaries lay 150–200 m higher than even today in spite of the recent rise of temperature to which we have already referred. Grapes were grown in England and East Prussia whereas today late frosts in spring now make this impossible. Storms over the North Sea and also possibly over the Atlantic were appreciably fewer then than they are today. Today the Vikings would not brave the open seas in their little boats which we see exhibited in museums in Oslo and Schleswig. The coasts of Iceland were for centuries almost completely free of ice. A thousand years ago, the Vikings travelled west-north-west right across the Straits of Denmark, whereas today drifting ice forces seafarers to go round the southern tip of Greenland. In Greenland itself there were sheep and woods in the south-west of the country where there was no ice; but there is very little information available in records on the great stretches of inland ice which were also there. There are some indications that the rather thin layer of inland ice in the north of Ellesmere Land, 82°N in the Canadian archipelago, was not formed until about 600 years ago, after this period.

But the favourable climatic conditions of the Middle Ages came to an end between 1300 and 1600, and a period of great weather variations set in, periods of extreme heat or extreme cold often lasting several decades and bringing agricultural crises in their train. The winter of 1322–3 was the severest ever recorded. Merchants then travelled across the ice from Rostock, and even Riga, to Sweden, and this would not have been possible since, even during the severe winters of 1939–40, 1941–2, and 1946–7. But it

74 Variations in C$_{14}$ activity
from 1203 BC to AD 1860.

211

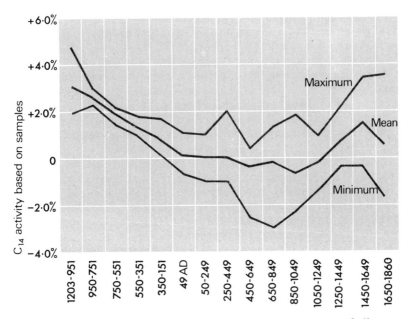

was in Iceland that there was the greatest deterioration of climate.
From 1540 and still more frequently after 1600, ice blocked the
coasts of Iceland on the average for 5–6 months, sometimes from
January into September each year, as opposed to 1 to 3 weeks
today.

The period 1600–50 is described as the 'little ice age'. This term
is a little exaggerated but not altogether unjustified. Alpine glaciers
attained their maximum extent in historical times and in their
advance buried pasture lands, passes and mines. Impressive
evidence of their retreat about 1820–50 can still be seen today in
the form of bare moraines. According to H. H. Lamb, polar sea ice
once stretched south almost to the Faroes and the Shetland Islands
covering several million km^2 of the Atlantic.

That there were similar glacier fluctuations in the west of North

America and in Patagonia has been determined by tree ring analysis. Yet glaciers did not reach the point of maximum advance in Norway and Alaska until about 1750.

The water level of the Caspian Sea and of the Italian lakes in the Middle Ages indicates that the climate of the Mediterranean area and the Near East must have been moist and cool. This was also the period of particularly high Nile floods, which suggests heavy summer rain in the Ethiopian Highlands. The statement that these were covered with snow at the time, although quite credible, must nevertheless be treated with reserve. It is remarkable that these obviously global climatic cycles also affected the eustatic movements of the sea level, according to R.W.Fairbridge. During the Rottnest transgression round about AD 800–1000, the level of the sea was about 80 cm higher than it is today, and during the Paria regression, in about AD 1500, it was about 2 m lower.

All these facts suggest the existence of characteristic anomalies in the circulation of the atmosphere which manifest themselves in a multiplicity of weather conditions. When the area of the polar sea covered by ice decreases, as today, then there is also a decrease in the meridional temperature difference, in which case there is also a decrease in the frequency of cyclone formations and the occurrence of violent storms. Numerous examples in the last decades bear witness to this fact. For instance, if a subtropical high in the Azores-Biscay area is diverted northward, then the westerlies are also diverted northward. The result is that there is a mild winter in western Europe and light rainfall in the central and eastern Mediterranean area. On the other hand, an advance of the ice boundary towards the south, particularly in the spring and summer, increases the temperature differences and consequently the frequency of storms over the Atlantic. At the same time, blocking high pressure zones with persisting meridional currents form more frequently, bringing extreme cold to some regions or extreme heat and precipitation to others. The relationships between distant circulation anomalies have already been discussed.

The latitude of the main frontal zone – the polar front used in the wider sense of this term – and the geographical location of the quasi-stationary highs are dependent on the slope of the meridional temperature gradient. However, we must not be tempted to attribute the existence of circulation anomalies simply to the spread of the Arctic sea ice which is, after all, driven by the wind, so that the location of its boundary is dependent on the distribution of air pressure and wind. Interactions and feed-back systems of this kind are very numerous in the atmosphere and this forces meteorologists to construct increasingly complicated mathematical and physical models to represent actual occurrences.

The climatic history of geological periods is very interesting indeed but, again, we cannot go into detail. The existence of several, probably five or six, glacial periods during the earliest period of geological history has been established without a shadow of doubt. The Pleistocene glaciation period, for example, is estimated to have lasted 1 to 1·5 million years. The last peak of the so-called 'Würm' glaciation period occurred only about 20,000 years ago. At that time gigantic ice domes which must have been 4,000 m high (estimated from the known compressibility of ice), existed on the North American continent and also over Europe, spreading out from Scandinavia and to a lesser extent from the Scottish highlands and the Alps. Over northern and eastern Siberia the ice shield was much flatter. The ice domes in North America covered an area of almost 16 million km^2 and about 10–11 million km^2 in Europe including western Siberia, as compared with an area of 12·7 million km^2 covered by the Antarctic ice today. Altogether the area of land covered by ice was about 45 million km^2 at that time, or about 9 % of the total area of the earth. Temperatures in the neighbourhood of these domes were about 10–13 °C below those of today. The climate in southern Germany, which lay at that time between the north European ice centre and the ice centre in the Alps, resembled that of the present climate in Labrador. The southern boundary of the ice caps reached in Russia a latitude of 50° and almost 38°N in North America, which is the latitude of Sicily! In the much greater areas with no

75 Climatic change in the Würm glacial period, with extended time scale. (After Büdel).
a = annual mean temperature in central Europe (Thuringia) ; **b** = eustatic change of sea level ;
A = Alleröd oscillation ; **B** = Bölling oscillation ;
C = Cochrane ice advance.

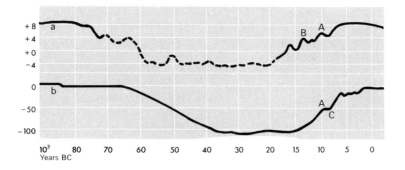

glaciers at all, temperatures were about 5°C lower that at the present day, according to evidence obtained in the tropics.

The great climatic belts also changed their extent or position. The main frontal zone in the Atlantic lay over southern Europe and included the Mediterranean; and winter rains extended to the central Sahara. The vast ice domes of the northern continents were taken from the water reservoir of the oceans, and their level eustatically fell 90 to 100 metres, in the great Riss Ice Age at least to 110 metres, perhaps for a shorter time even to 135 metres.

These world-wide glacials, which occurred simultaneously in both hemispheres, were interrupted by warm interglacials lasting at least some 10,000 years. During these warm periods, the ice-caps of the northern continents completely melted, and the ocean level rose above its present level. During an early interglacial (Sizil, cf. table 10) the oceans rose to nearly 100 metres above their present level; at this time the Antarctic ice-cap, which almost certainly survived all interglacials, obviously was shallow. Considering the vegetation pattern during the warm periods, the average temperatures should have been about 2 degrees higher than today.

A similar warm period occurred 4,500 to 6,000 years ago, that is. after the last glaciation, known as the post-glacial warm period. At this time, most Alpine glaciers had disappeared, in Siberia

Table 9 Tropical climatic levels

Mean annual temperature	Approximate height (m)	South and Central America	Ethiopia	Typical crops
24–28°	0–800	Tierra caliente	Kolla	Cocoa, Bananas
18–24°	800–1600	Tierra templada	Woina Dega	Coffee
12–18°	1600–2700	Tierra fria	Dega	Corn, Fruit
6–12°	2700–3800	Paramo	–	Meadow grass Potatoes
under 6°	above 3800	Tierra helada	–	None

forests extended nearly to the northern coasts, and permafrost survived only in Yakutia. Simultaneously the climate of the Sahara and the Near East was more humid than today, and deserts were widely changed into steppes. The sea level rose to 3–5 m above present levels (former Peron transgression).

Figure 75 shows the very great amount of variations in climate that have occurred in the 15,000 years of the *post-glacial period*. Further details, unfortunately, cannot be given here. The variations during the comparatively short period of the Alleröd stage are particularly marked. From the facts we have considered it is quite clear that we are at present living in an interglacial period and that in a few thousand years we can expect the advent of a new glacial period. It is also clear, however, that man is interfering more and more with the total radiation, heat, and water balances whose time variations reflect variations in the physical processes that cause them and so we hardly dare make any forecasts.

One of the most astonishing discoveries in geology, however, is not that such glacial periods have already existed several times in the history of our globe (at the beginning of the Cambrian period 550 million years ago, during the transition between the Carboniferous and Permian periods about 250 million years ago and during the Pleistocene period) but that both poles, apart from

Table 10 Cold (C) and warm (W) periods in the Pleistocene period and eustatic variations of sea level

	Alps	North Sea area	North America	Sea level Stage	metres	Time* from today × 1000 years
C	Würm	Weichsel	Wisconsin	–	−90 to 100	20–60
W	R–W	Eem	Sangamon	Monastir	+8 to 18	–
C	Riss	Saale	Illinoian	–	−100 to 110	110–130
W	M–R	Holstein	Yarmouth	Tyrrhen	+32 to 40	–
C	Mindel	Elster	Kansan	–	−70 to 80?	180–120
W	G–M	Cromer	Aftonian	Milazzo	+55 to 60	–
C	Günz	Weybourne	Nebraskan	–	?	270–320
W	D–G	Tegelen	–	Sizil	+90 to 100	–
C	Donau	Brüggen	–	–	?	–

* Estimated on the Emiliani or Wundt-van Woerkom 'short' time scale.
An absolute time scale over the last 600,000 years is still not settled: there exist two other time scales today. For the glacial periods the figures they give are respectively 2 and 4–5 times higher than the above figures.

a few local mountain glaciers, were free of ice for at least 90% of the known history of the earth. It is therefore one of the most interesting tasks of meteorologists to study the circulation of the atmosphere in this context, for which there is no parallel on earth during present times.

7 Weather and climate modification

7 Weather and climate modification

We know from the study of the physics of clouds that many hundreds of thousands or millions of cloud droplets must join together to form a single raindrop. This occurs naturally as soon as the temperature of the cloud falls below about $-10°C$, provided that a sufficient number of ice particles are present, or at temperatures above $0°C$ if a sufficient number of larger drops are present. This opens up the possibility of inducing the process artificially or at any rate accelerating it.

Since 1948 numerous large-scale attempts have been made in many countries to do this by feeding solid carbon-dioxide (dry ice) particles into clouds which are at a temperature of between $0°$ and $-10°C$, or by feeding larger drops of water into warm clouds (temperature above $0°C$). Laboratory experiments by V. Schaefer in 1946 showed that fine hexagonal crystals of silver iodide were so similar to natural ice crystals that they could induce ice formation. When aircraft drop such crystals of silver iodide into a supercooled cloud slight precipitation frequently occurs within 10–30 minutes. This method can be used to clear supercooled fog from the runways of airports when the temperature is below $0°C$. Unfortunately fog mostly occurs when the temperature is above the freezing point of water and this method is useless for clearing 'warm' fogs. Experiments to clear fog by feeding large drops of water into it from above have yielded controversial results, but in any case the practical possibilities of this method are very limited. Water-vapour in the atmosphere resulting from combustion processes on earth can in fact cause the formation of very persistent ice fogs, as for instance, in Alaska.

The inoculation of upward billowing cloud banks with silver iodide crystals dropped from aircraft can often induce the precipitation process and cause showers to fall. However, this is most effective when in the vicinity the natural precipitation process has already begun. But to be of any importance in agriculture, or as a source of additional water for other purposes, a precipitation of at least 2·5 mm is generally required. Anything less merely moistens the surface of the ground. Moreover, when the weather is dry and the clouds are high in the sky, much of the falling rain will evaporate before reaching the ground, and can often be clearly seen as a ragged curtain of raindrops, known as *virga*, beneath the clouds.

Less effective and more costly is an earlier idea of introducing silver iodide crystals into the ascending air currents below billowing clouds. Since it is not possible to predict the time and place of the appearance of such cloud banks, this method requires a whole network of silver iodide burners and a large number of people to man them. Another point against it is that under the influence of solar radiation, crystals of silver iodide seem to lose some of their power to initiate precipitation. All the experiments that have been carried out so far in the middle and higher latitudes under carefully controlled conditions have yielded results which, when compared with events in a control area, did not have any statistical significance.

Only under special conditions, particularly along the windward slopes of mountains near the sea where moist maritime air is almost constantly rising and condensing, has it been possible to increase the amount of precipitation by 10–20%. This has been shown in a series of systematic experiments lasting over several years in such places as the seaward side of the coastal ranges of California and Oregon, and it would be possible also at the coastal mountains of central Chile, north-west Spain, and Norway. In most instances, success was achieved in regions which were already naturally rainy but where the supply of water was nevertheless insufficient to meet the requirement of hydro-electric projects, or cities near arid regions, like those in California.

Recent experiments have demonstrated that under certain conditions in tropical and subtropical areas a single upward billowing cloud can be made to develop at an explosive rate by the use of massive quantities of silver iodide. This is because of the latent heat released when water freezes. But this process has an adverse effect on surrounding clouds over a large area. The effect is to produce heavy precipitation in a small area rather than to

76 The effect of seeding on a tropical cumulus cloud. *Top left* shows the cloud at the time of seeding. Some upward growth had already commenced and the cloud was thus a likely candidate for seeding. *Bottom left* was taken after nine minutes and just prior to its maximum vertical extent. *Top right* was taken

19 minutes after seeding ; the cloud was developing horizontally and the first sign of the ice phase could be observed near the summit of the cloud. *Bottom right* was taken 38 minutes after seeding and a characteristic cumulonimbus anvil developed.

increase precipitation evenly over a large one. The water content of shallow clouds is so small that they cannot provide much precipitation. The most common forms of cloud – stratus, stratocumulus, and shallow cumulus, have a maximum water content of 1 gram per cubic metre. Assuming a cloud thickness of 1,000 m, and ignoring any possible losses by evaporation, the maximum amount of rain that such a cloud can produce is 1 litre per square metre or a rainfall of 1 mm which is just sufficient to moisten the ground, and no more. Nature has therefore set very narrow limits within which it is possible to increase precipitation artificially by microphysical processes.

What would be of considerable importance in many countries is an effective way of controlling or eliminating damage caused by hail. This applies particularly to the foothill regions of the Alps in the south of France and the north of Italy, and in central and southern parts of North America and Russia. One approach is to prevent the further growth of ice particles in supercooled clouds by producing an excessive number of nuclei. This was tried in Switzerland, near Locarno, in a series of experiments lasting over 5 years, silver iodide being introduced from the ground into upward billowing clouds. But the results obtained did not show any appreciable difference between the frequency of hailstorms in the district in which the experiments were carried out and that in neighbouring control districts where clouds were not subjected to any treatment. Other scientists, notably in the USSR and North America, have however carried out experiments which are claimed to have met with more success. These involved the use of grenades and rockets to shoot silver iodide into the zone of clouds where supercooled droplets form, thus inducing precipitation before the hail formation stage was reached.

Experiments have also been made using explosive shells fired into the clouds and even tolling church bells. Many such experiments are nothing more than traditional folklore magic. In 1902, an international commission concluded, after thorough investigation, that such methods were completely useless and the Empress

Maria Theresia of Austria 200 years ago issued an edict forbidding such 'blasphemous hail shooting'. Recent research, however, has suggested that the shock waves of explosions may shatter hailstones, many of which have radial fracture lines within them. The small pieces of ice would then melt more easily during their fall. Millions of dollars are, in fact, spent each year upon rockets fired into thunder clouds in the agricultural areas of northern Italy, southern France, and several other countries including the United States, Russia, Kenya and South Africa.

One of the basic problems of rain-making is that where artificially produced precipitation is particularly wanted, which is in the arid and semi-arid areas, it is not possible to produce it. Where there is no cloud, or where the water content of the clouds is too small, no method can produce an effective amount of precipitation.

It is known, of course, that the hot air currents rising from great conflagrations, particularly those that occurred during the last war, lead to the formation of thick cumulonimbus clouds. The energy involved is enormous, and an experiment carried out in France in which 100 oil burners each burned 1 ton of fuel oil per hour produced only little effect. The burning of natural vegetation such as savannahs, which is done regularly, is occasionally effective in producing clouds but has so many disadvantages that it is certainly not a practical technique. It should be mentioned in this connection, however, that the growth of our big cities has resulted in an increase in the number of showers and thunderstorms that occur on their lee side. The reason for this is an increase of surface friction due to the irregularity of the ground and increased thermal turbulence owing to the warmth of city air.

The experiments carried out by J. S. Malkus on the possibilities of influencing tropical hurricanes have aroused great interest. The basic idea was that if the upward movement of air at the outer edge of the wall of the hurricane could be accelerated, the rate of vertical exchange of air would be increased, and this in turn could lead to a diminution of the wind velocity in the lower layers. Such acceleration could, it was argued, be effected by feeding silver iodide nuclei

77 Percentage changes in mean annual rainfall from 1925 to 59, compared with 1898–1924. Areas above 1000 feet O.D. are grey. The 7·03 per cent isoline encloses the area of significant rainfall increase.

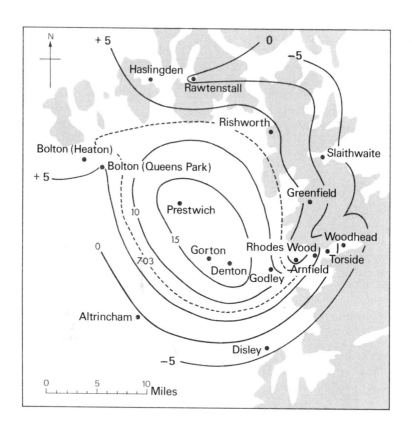

into upward building billowing clouds, as was done in experiments to prevent the formation of hail. The experiments to test this theory were planned and carried out on a large scale, but they have not yielded any definite results, and their theoretical basis is still under discussion. If, however, it were possible to reduce the evaporation of seawater, which is the most important source of energy of these destructive storms, a great step forward would have been taken towards the solution of this problem. So far as we are concerned, however, the very fact that such large-scale experiments are planned and carried out at all, is important. Today there is no longer any doubt that within very narrow and strictly defined bounds it is possible to interfere with the complex mechanisms of the atmosphere which involve huge amounts of energy.

Influencing microclimates

Meteorological processes close to the ground are extraordinarily sensitive to deliberate or accidental interference by man. For instance, for centuries man has burned savannahs over huge areas at the end of the dry winter season. (Possible conclusions from this with reference to climate on a large scale will be discussed later.)

Let us first of all look at the simple case of a hilly or mountainous region. There, on clear radiation nights, cold air forms on the slopes and in accordance with the laws of gravity, flows downward and gathers in the deepest hollows in the valley. The formation of such lakes of cold air is favoured whenever the valley or hollow is closed in by the terrain. When the temperature in these cold air lakes reaches the dew-point they become visible as knee-high fog patches which later develop in size and extent. If a railway or road embankment is built in such a valley, colder air accumulates behind it creating a reservoir of cold air and increasing the danger of night frosts on nearby slopes. This weak but nonetheless effective nocturnal cold air stream can, however, easily be diverted by the planting of trees or hedges in appropriate places. If a water-storage reservoir is built in such a hollow, it will act like any other lake,

absorbing and storing the radiant heat during the day and liberating it at night so that the risk of frost in its surrounding area is considerably reduced.

Among the outstanding examples of frost hollows are those in natural sink holes in the Austrian Alps. In one of these deep limestone sink holes – the Gstettner Alm in the Dead Mountains in upper Austria, the natural vegetation is of the subarctic type. Records covering many years show that the lowest temperatures during every winter lie between −45° and −53°C, which are the lowest temperatures ever recorded in Europe. In isolated cases the temperature on the floor of this hollow is up to 30°C below that of the temperature around its rim. The subarctic vegetation in this *frost hollow* is a proof of the frequent occurrence of these extreme conditions.

The trees and hedges planted by man in stormy regions like Brittany and windy countries from Britain to Denmark and southern Norway have a considerable effect on the climate close to the ground. Whenever the movement of the wind along the ground is effectively braked, there is a simultaneous diminution in

78 Dense mist filling one of the deep valleys in Skye, Scotland. The mist entered the far valley from the north (from the left). The near valley is clear of mist because it is enclosed by the Cuillins to the north, which prevented fog penetration.
79 Distribution of temperature on 21 January 1930 in the Gstettneralm sink-hole near Lunz. Vegetation in the sink-hole is obviously affected by the low temperatures.

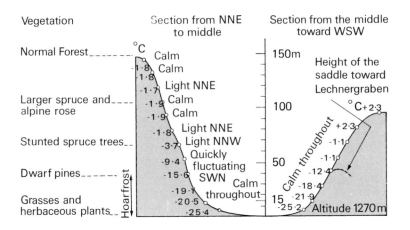

Vegetation	Section from NNE to middle	Section from the middle toward WSW
Normal Forest	°C Calm	150m
	1·8 Calm	Height of the saddle toward Lechnergraben
	1·8	
	1·7 Light NNE	
Larger spruce and alpine rose	1·9 Calm	100 °C +2·3
	1·9 Calm	+2·3
	1·8 Light NNE	1·1
Stunted spruce trees	3·7 Light NNW	
	Quickly	1·1
Dwarf pines	9·4 fluctuating	50 12·4
	15·6 SWN	18·4
	Calm	21·9
Grasses and herbaceous plants	19·1 throughout	15 25·2 Altitude 1270m
	20·5	
	25·4	

(Hoarfrost; Calm throughout)

evaporation and in the carbon dioxide exchange in the air close to the ground. Both these effects of windbreaks can be of great importance in the growing of crops. Windbreaks on a huge scale have been planted in many countries in the last 10–15 years but particularly in the steppes of southern Russia, where this method has been used to reduce the dessicating effect of the strong dry south-east winds which occur very frequently there in the spring. If the ground is very dry, strong winds will whirl the topmost fertile layer into the air causing dust storms which in the course of years will severely reduce the fertility of the land. Dust storms originating in the Ukraine have on several occasions travelled across Hungary and Rumania into central Europe. The same danger threatened the boundary region of the dry prairie areas in the United States, particularly in 1932–5. After 1940, however, there was a moist period which temporarily removed this danger but the threat remains, as it always does in semi-arid regions.

The protection of fruit trees and vineyards against frost in the late spring is obviously very important since this is the time when plants and trees are most susceptible to damage. Frost can occur on any clear night but particularly when the airflow is of polar origin and it can cause really heavy damage. But since such frosts are generally restricted to a shallow air layer close to the ground, there are a number of means of preventing their occurrence. The simplest consists in burning coke or oil in stoves distributed at strategic intervals over the danger area in such a way that each stove will raise the air temperature by 2–4°C, over an area of 30–50 metres radius. Another method consists of producing an artificial fog or smoke blanket which reduces radiation heat losses from the ground. This leads to a marked increase in the nocturnal counter-radiation of the atmosphere. A third method consists in creating turbulence in the layers of the air close to the ground by means of giant fans so as to prevent the development of an inversion immediately over the ground. Finally, there is a method which consists in spraying the danger area with water or flooding it. The freezing water droplets release so much latent heat that the temperature of the moistened plants cannot fall appreciably below the freezing point and thus they remain safe beneath a mantle of ice. All these methods have their advantages and disadvantages, but the decision as to which to apply must depend on local conditions.

In subarctic regions like northern Russia, Siberia and Alaska, the snow cover lasts into June and prevents the utilisation of the intense summer radiation for such purposes as growing vegetables. Coal dust spread over the snow cover reduces the albedo of the snow from 80% to 30–40%, which helps to accelerate the thawing process, and as a result produces an earlier and more intense surface thawing of the frozen ground. This method has apparently already yielded good results in the Russian subarctic region.

Such artificial influencing of individual factors of the radiation and heat budget plays an important role not only in the local microclimate but also in the macroclimate. This applies particularly to such fundamental transformations of the landscape as, for instance, the drainage of swamps, and irrigation in arid areas. In its original state a swamp stores a large amount of heat which it releases during the night or during the cold periods of the year. By far the largest amount of the incoming radiation absorbed during the day is used for evaporation so that the direct heating of the air is only slight. But once the swamp has been drained, evaporation decreases very appreciably and a much greater proportion of the incoming radiation balance is available for the direct heating of the air. But a drained swamp is an extraordinarily poor conductor of heat and its capacity to store heat is also very slight. Reversing the former process, the drained swamp area now becomes hotter during the day and colder during the night. Thus even in summer drained swamp areas become cold sources. For instance, in the drained swamp areas near Kaiserslautern, in the upper Rhine region, where summer days are warm, night frosts occur to the detriment of local agriculture.

Even more impressive, however, are the changes in the heat budget brought about when an irrigated oasis is created in an arid region. The albedo of a light coloured desert sand is generally relatively high – about 25–30%, whereas that of watered arable land is about 10–15%. In the desert there is very little or no water for evaporation so that all the incoming radiation is available for the direct heating of the air. Over an oasis, however, the incoming energy (by radiation and advection) is used up almost entirely for evaporating water. Thus, direct heating of the air above an oasis is very slight and when, during the day, hot dry desert air moves over the oasis, it is cooled from below, releasing energy which also becomes available for evaporating water. In this way more energy can be used advectively for evaporation than is available from the radiation balance. Thus we see that it is possible for two neighbouring areas with completely different heat budgets to be separated by a sharp dividing line. On one side of this line is desert and on the other the oasis. Such situations are found, for instance in the Nile Valley and in the area of the Indus where the area irrigated artificially is about 80,000 km^2.

Another technically feasible method of modifying climate consists in accelerating the thermal convection process by changing the nature of the surface of the ground, by covering it, for instance, with a layer of asphalt which has good insulating properties and a small albedo.

Of the greatest importance, so far as the modification of climates is concerned, would be a means of reducing the massive losses of water by evaporation from reservoirs, canals and rivers in arid areas. This can be done by covering the surface of the water with a monomolecular layer of various long chain alcohols, such as cetyl alcohol. In the laboratory, evaporation can be reduced by about 50% using this method, but the figure drops to 10–20% when the experiment is carried out in the open air, where moderate wind breaks the film and drives its residue towards the shore.

Influencing the macroclimate

A rise in the content of carbon dioxide in the whole of the atmosphere since 1880 has aroused a great deal of lively discussion. Even though the average proportion of this gas in the atmosphere rose only from 290 to 330 parts per million or about 12%, this fact is nonetheless alarming because the increase is related mainly to the increase in the combustion of coal and mineral oil by industry. But it has been frequently pointed out, though admittedly without any quantitative evidence, that the pollution of the atmosphere by soot and dust must also have increased globally, and not just locally. Both processes have the same effect; they increase the absorption of radiation in the infra-red range of the spectrum, thereby increasing the amount of counter-radiation and reducing the net loss of radiation from the earth. Since the average temperature of the near-surface layers of air has almost everywhere risen by about 0·01°C a year since 1880, a strong suspicion exists that this overall rise in temperature, with its world-wide consequences, has been unintentionally caused by man: an anthropogenic modification of climate on a large scale. It appears to be all the more significant because the amount of energy derived from fossilised fuel has been increasing from year to year.

80 Carbon dioxide content of free air in northern Atlantic region during 1870–1956.

233

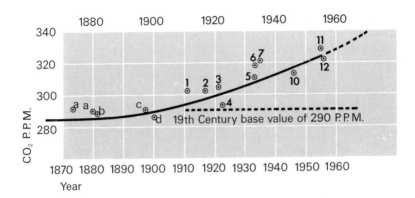

Incidentally, it was a small part of the radiation balance during the geological periods long past that photosynthesised the living matter which today, in fossilised form, we use as fuel.

This problem is obviously important enough to be considered in all its various aspects. The CO_2 content of the atmosphere in the Northern Hemisphere fluctuates by a small amount with the seasons. This is caused by the summer growth of vegetation in middle and higher latitudes leading to seasonal interchanges of CO_2 between the two hemispheres.

If the CO_2 content of the atmosphere has increased by about 12% as the result of the additions of CO_2 from fossilised sources, we would expect a corresponding decrease in the amount of radio active carbon, C_{14}, in the atmosphere because the CO_2 from fossilised sources does not contain C_{14}, whose half-life period is 5,700 years. Yet calculation of the C_{14} content of tree rings shows a diminution of only 2–4% in the last 60–80 years. This could, of course, be the result of the storage of CO_2 in the seas, but there is another source of CO_2 for which man is responsible. This is the production by soil bacteria of CO_2 in quantities that can no longer be completely used up by plants because of the destruction of much natural vegetation and the conversion of land to agricultural use.

In addition there is the CO_2 produced by the bush fires caused by natives in the savannah lands. According to admittedly approximate estimates, the amount of carbon dioxide produced in this way is almost equivalent to that produced by industry. At any rate, this additional supply of C_{14} containing carbon dioxide could be the explanation of the discrepancy to which we have just referred. Unfortunately, however, we cannot go into the complicated exchange of CO_2 between the atmosphere, the oceans, plants, and animal life.

The figure obtained by Plass in 1956 for the rise in temperature due to CO_2 was $0.011°C$, which seems to agree exactly (and perhaps too exactly) with the figure for the overall increase in temperature in the atmosphere. The effect is important not only in relation to our ideas on climatic cycles but also because it seems to provide clear evidence to support the suggestion that the overall global increase in temperature is due directly to the industrial, agricultural, and other activities of man. In chapter 6, however, we saw that the overall global temperature had ceased to increase between 1945–50 or at least that it had come to a temporary standstill in spite of the fact that the combustion of fossilised fuels had continued to increase. This is a convincing counter-argument.

In 1963, Möller pointed out that the temperature rise might be due not only to a rise in the CO_2 content of the atmosphere by about 10%, but also to a rise in its moisture content by about 3%, or a 1% increase in cloud. While this is certainly possible, there is no real evidence to support such a contention.

The whole question in fact is still open but we must expect a steady increase in the CO_2 content of the atmosphere up to about 500 parts per million in view of the continually increasing quantities of energy we are using. We must therefore continue to study this CO_2 problem with great care because failure to do so might bring consequences whose gravity can hardly be over-estimated. It is generally admitted today that the fluctuating CO_2 content of the atmosphere is linked with the whole problem of climatic cycles: what is still disputed is the extent and importance of the relatively small fluctuations that have occurred in recent years. If we use a geological time scale we have to add yet another factor – the production of 'juvenile' CO_2 by volcanoes, which were probably much more frequent in some early periods in the history of the earth than they are today.

From time to time we read in the press and in science fiction about sensational large-scale plans for changing the climate artificially. Most of these stem from engineers with only a superficial knowledge of the physics of the atmosphere. One such plan that excited much attention was the so-called 'Atlantropa-Plan'. It involved erecting a barrier across the Straits of Gibraltar, following which, surface water from the Congo was to be led into the central part of the Sahara where it would form a lake with an area of 2-million km^2 – about four times the size of France. This was supposed to transform the very arid climate of the Sahara into a humid climate with plentiful rainfall. If we examine this plan carefully, ignoring all possible political complications, we see that it is based on the assumption that the rapid evaporation of water in an arid climate is alone sufficient to produce copious rainfalls. This is proved wrong by the situation over the Red Sea, and even more strikingly over the Atlantic Ocean between the latitudes 15–30°N and 0–15°S where, at any rate in the eastern and central part of this region, the rainfall is almost as slight as that in the Sahara. The Island of Daedalus in the Red Sea (24°N) and the Ascension Island (8°S) in the middle of the southern Atlantic are as bare as a desert, receiving rainfalls of only 7 and 65 mm a year respectively.

This idea is not unconnected with the present extension of the Aswan Dam in the valley of the Nile. The lake behind the Aswan Dam, which is about 600 km long, but only a few km broad, is located in a zone in which the incoming radiation is at its strongest and tremendous amounts of energy are available for evaporating water. Moreover, besides the energy from the radiation balance, the dry, hot, desert winds bring additional energy to this area during the day. The evaporation from this long stretch of water is certainly greater than that over the open sea: the actual amount is estimated at about 250 cm a year, although it may be as much as 300–350 cm a year by contrast with the considerably broader Red Sea, where it is 210 cm a year. The estimates in specialist literature about ten years ago fluctuated between 10 m and as little as 150 cm a year, but both figures were based on unrealistic assumptions.

The prevailing northerly and easterly airstreams carry the moisture that has evaporated from the waters of the Aswan Dam lake into the central areas of the Sahara but do not increase the moisture in the atmosphere in that area to any appreciable extent. Incidentally, because of the high temperatures there, the absolute water-vapour content of the atmosphere over the Sahara is almost the same as that in the humid atmosphere above western Europe. In the summer this amount would correspond to a precipitation of 1·5 to 3 cm, compared with 2 cm over western France. The aridity of the Sahara is due entirely to the subsidence of air related to the general circulation of the whole atmosphere. Only in exceptional circumstances does this allow deep upward movements of air to take place with the formation of clouds followed by precipitation. Such precipitation could be induced by, for instance, daytime slope winds at the high mountains of Tibesti and Hoggar under very special weather conditions.

In 1959 the great Swedish meteorologist T. Bergeron suggested a project based on sound meteorological principles. This involved the area of the so-called Sudan belt about 10–17°N which is visited every summer by tropical rains. It is part of a belt stretching from the west coast of Africa, across the whole continent to the steep slopes of the Ethiopian mountain barrier. In summer SW and W winds predominate in this zone in the lower layers of the atmosphere up to a height of about 1,500–2,000 m. They contain water-vapour from the forests of the Congo basin. The horizontal transport here is relatively small because an E–NE air flow in the upper layers opposes the W–SW flow in the lower layers. What Bergeron suggested was that in the first place the two great rivers, the Nile and the Niger, which flow from the humid rain forests into an arid region, should be used exclusively for irrigation. In addition, the water of the Congo should be brought across a low barrier to Lake Chad, which has an area of about 20,000 km², around which there are vast expanses of land suitable for irrigation. The artificial irrigation of large areas of land the size of France and the Federal Republic of Germany would give rise to summer evaporation in quantities equivalent to those from an open water surface. This would raise the water-vapour content of the air in an area where in the summer, in contrast to what happens over the Sahara, there is widespread convection within air generally moving upward. Today we know a little more about the complicated dynamics of these vertical movements during the summer, which are related to the presence and properties of the tropical easterly jet stream originating in southern Asia. The author found that the velocity of both these large-scale vertical movements of air – downward over the Sahara, and upward over the Sudan belt – is about 1 cm a second, or about 1 km a day. This seems very slow but we must not forget that the areas over which this takes place cover no less than 4–7 million km². Any increase in the water-vapour content of the atmosphere in the Sudan belt which is bounded on the north, towards the Sahara, by the intertropical convergence zone would lead during the summer rainy season to an increase in the amount of precipitation over the whole of this climatic area, because the distances involved in the horizontal transport of vapour are small (about 200–500 km a day). Since the thickness of the humid W–SW air stream decreases as it approaches the ITC, there is a belt 200–250 km broad south of the ITC where the rainfall is still very small. It is possible that the addition of water-vapour to the atmosphere in this belt could lead to an increase of the area over which the summer rains fall.

Bergeron further suggests that the evaporation of the sea water near the coasts of the Gulf of Guinea could be accelerated by heating or even, if necessary, boiling the water there, using atomic energy, which in the future will be much cheaper than it is today. This would make sense where the vertically integrated water-vapour transport in the troposphere is directed landward. This, however, is no longer the case at the height of summer in July and August at latitudes north of 11–12°N, where the upper easterly flow directs the total transport of water-vapour in the direction of the Atlantic.

The political problems would, perhaps, be more difficult to solve and would require effective and very close co-operation between the emergent African states. At all events the meteorological-climatological basis of Bergeron's proposal seems to be sound. The direction and intensity of the water-vapour transport can be determined empirically and explained on theoretical grounds. The path along which the water-vapour is transported in the southern portion of the Sudan belt ends at the 2,500–3,000 m high barrier of the Ethiopian mountains where there is the greatest rainfall in this area. Any increase in the amount of water-vapour in this zone would therefore benefit the whole of the Nile area, including Egypt. Bergeron points out that his proposal involves using the same quantity of water over and over again by an alternating process of evaporation and precipitation.

An even more far reaching proposal to influence climate is receiving serious attention even though it will probably not be realised for some time. The proposal was made independently by two far-sighted meteorologists: H. Wexler, the research director of the US Weather Bureau until his recent death, and M. I. Budyko, the director of the main geophysical observatory of the USSR. Both based their proposal on a large-scale meteorological phenomenon, the fact that the ice cover on the Arctic seas – in a geological time scale – is not permanent and when it does exist it is subject to considerable variations in thickness and area.

In chapter 6 we discussed the subject of the Arctic sea ice cover and its variation in size and position over the years. We noted that its area had increased since the Middle Ages by about 20%, and that during the interglacial periods it apparently had ceased to exist altogether. In the last few centuries its thickness has varied from 250 to 150 cm.

During the international geophysical year both American and Russian scientists spent a great deal of time and energy investigating the heat and water budget of the sea ice. The results showed that the summer thaw was limited to $2\frac{1}{2}$ months and could not set in before the protective snow cover, with its high albedo, had melted away. The 25 cm thick ice layer which melts during the summer period, freezes again from below during the winter period when heat flows from the unfrozen sea water (at a temperature of just below freezing), to the radiating surface of the ice over which the average air temperature is between $-30°$ and $-35°$C. Calculations made by Budyko show that although these processes are in equilibrium today, present climatic conditions make it impossible for new ice layers to form in the Arctic Ocean far from the coast once the ice has disappeared by one or another process. One of the most telling arguments is that the absorption and storage of large quantities of solar radiation by the open oceans during the summer must lead, within a short time, to appreciably greater sea temperatures during the winter. The stored solar energy here is much greater than the heat transported by the Gulf Stream and its tributaries. The advection of very cold continental air from the land masses of Siberia and northern Canada would then lead only to the formation of a new coastal ice strip some 100–200 km wide.

If we could spread soot or coal dust on to the snow of the ice floes in the month of May, at the beginning of the period of maximum solar radiation, we would reduce the albedo of the snow cover from 75–80 % to 40–50 % which would result in a lengthening of the summer thaw period and an increase in ablation by about one half. Naturally this is an oversimplified picture and the problem could hardly be solved in detail at present. The cost would be of the same order as that expected to be spent on spectacular space research in the next few decades by the two great world powers. Such an investment is justified only if the outcome of such a project can be predicted with confidence, if it is really worthwhile, and if the international co-operation that would be required could be assured. But since modification of the climate figures in the programme of the Soviet Union, other countries must also be aware of this problem. The idea, in fact, might not be as fanciful as we might at first believe.

Let us however assume that such a large-scale operation has actually been carried out and the Arctic sea ice disappears completely in summer, while in winter it limits itself to a 100–200 km broad strip along the coasts rather like the strip today along the coast of Labrador. Under these circumstances, in summer the surface temperature of the sea in the central zone at a latitude of 80°N would be +2°C to +5°C or more (today it is 0°C), but in winter it would be 0°C to −2°C, as compared with −30° to −35°C today. We can also estimate what would happen to the temperature of the troposphere, to be compared, for instance, with the recent state above Bear Island at a latitude of 78°N (longitude 19°E) in the open sea within the North Atlantic Drift. The result would be an increase of average temperature in the troposphere of between 2–3°C in the summer, as opposed to 5–6°C in the winter today. The relatively slight increase in winter compared with the figure of 30°C at the ground is explained by the absence of a ground inversion. The intensity of the atmospheric circulation, however, depends primarily on the average tropospheric temperature difference between the equator and the pole (see chapter 3), and especially on the strength of the extratropical westerly winds and the latitudinal location of the subtropical high pressure cells. If we take as our reference layer, the layer between 700 and 100 mb (3–16 km), which alone is sufficiently comparable, this temperature difference today has an average value of 14·4°C in the Northern Hemisphere and of 26·6°C in the Southern Hemisphere. These figures show that with a further decrease in the temperature gradient the temperature difference would be reduced to about 11°C, or only 40% of the figure for the Southern Hemisphere. This in turn would lead to a further weakening of the westerly winds which in winter would correspond to what they are today in May or September. The tropical high pressure cells would move northward by about 5–6° of latitude, whereupon the subtropical winter rains would disappear in southern California, the central Mediterranean Sea area (south of a latitude of about 37°), Asia Minor, and in the Punjab. The asymmetric nature of the meteorological equator would become more marked and its position would move 2–300 km further north. The result of this would be that the north-eastern portion of Brazil, the African coast around the mouth of the Congo river, and various areas in East Africa would lie in a permanently arid zone.

All these conclusions can be verified approximately by circulation models and such calculations are being carried out now or are in the process of preparation. But even if the realisation of such a project is still far away, the fact is that the problem exists and we must make sure that we appreciate in good time the full extent of all the consequences that its solution would bring.

Nor is this the only problem. Our knowledge of the radiation and heat budget of the earth's surface and of the atmosphere opens up a path to the large-scale modification of climate, for some of the factors of the heat budget are very sensitive to man's interference. They are the factors that create the climate and these have been studied in recent years by Russian and other scientists with a great deal of energy and initiative. Obviously this is one of the great tasks for the meteorologists of the future.

Looking ahead

If we review the present and future possibilities of modifying the weather and climate we come to the conclusion that it would be easier to influence the heat budget of the earth's surface than the microphysical processes occurring in clouds. For the clouds are in a constant state of rapid transformation involving shape, structure, and location, and it is very difficult to gain a full understanding of these and their relationships and to control them. This means that modifying *climate* would appear to be a very much simpler operation than influencing the *weather*. But any modification of the climate on a large scale involving, say, 10^5 to 10^6 square kilometres, will naturally have considerable side effects on the weather, for, of course, climate is the sum of all weather processes.

However sceptical we may be about the prospects of influencing the weather directly by the application of our knowledge of cloud physics, it may well be that if we take into consideration the processes involved in the radiation and heat balance our attitude will one day prove to have been unjustified, at any rate so far as some areas of our planet are concerned.

The total amount of precipitation on earth (N_E) is constant today. Any interference in the precipitation process in one place merely results in a redistribution of precipitation so long as the total amount of evaporation (V_E), 90% of which comes from the seas, is not susceptible to increase. Such a possibility might, however, become fact in the foreseeable future if the use of heat produced by thermo-nuclear fusion becomes a viable proposition. From the beginning of history man has interfered with the heat budget of the earth's surface. Changing the natural landscape in itself is an interference with the radiation and heat balance, but the importance of this is still recognised by only a few. Forest fires, the transformation of forests and woods into arable land, meadows, and grass land, the intentional bush fires during the dry seasons in the tropics – all these interfere with nature. And so does the drainage of swamps and bogs, the acceleration of the flow of rivers by straightening their beds, and artificial irrigation. This interference with nature over thousands of years has transformed the surface of the earth. This applies also to the heat budget: the albedo, the effective terrestrial radiation, the relationship between the turbulent transport of heat and of water-vapour are all physical entities with which man can and does interfere without much difficulty. We would not be very far wrong if we said that in one way or another man has transformed the nature of at least 20–25% of the land surface on our globe, or about 30–40 million m^2. Moreover, this process will be further accelerated by the rapid increase of the world's population.

The world's population is increasing today at the rate of

60–65 million a year, so that the total population in the year 2000 is likely to be above 5,000 million, as compared with 2,000 million in 1925 and 3,000 million in 1960. And so we come face to face with the problem first posed by Malthus – providing food for a world population increasing in a geometrical progression. Meanwhile, we are beginning gradually to understand the physical and climatological processes involved in the transformation of the landscape and to apply them. Today, only a small minority of scientists is concerned, and so plans involving the transformation of landscapes are made and executed without any clear understanding of the consequences that might follow. Some of these consequences, such as the destruction of forests in the Mediterranean mountain areas, are irreversible. This also applies particularly to the continental areas in the subtropics and tropics where the radiation processes are very much more intense but the advection processes very much weaker than in the European countries of middle and high latitudes. In the tropics and the subtropics, there is no compensation by air masses brought from elsewhere which is a dominating feature of our climate. Any kind of interference therefore can have both favourable and unfavourable effects on the environment. For this reason the greatest caution must be exercised in the planning and execution of projects that might influence weather or climate. We cannot arrest the present population explosion of our times. All we can do is to hope that the number of people on earth will be stabilised at a not too high level by the beginning of the 21st century without any great social or political unrest. But in any case the situation demands that we exercise the utmost care to ensure that we utilise the treasures of nature and natural energy in the most efficient manner possible.

Water is today becoming a raw material more valuable than coal or mineral oil, and a water supply will always remain a problem even if it became possible to desalinate sea water economically. The water budget, however, is a critical component of the heat and radiation budget, for we have seen that evaporation of water uses

70–80% of the available net radiation balance. Consequently, irresponsible interference with these balances without regard to possible long-term consequences, is something we cannot afford today, for, as we have seen, some of the consequences are irreversible. Foresters and farmers have recognised this after many bitter experiences, but engineers and politicians are unfortunately still not sufficiently aware of its importance. But if we do not act today in accordance with this knowledge, our children and grandchildren will hold us responsible for a wanton rape of nature and the squandering of its rich treasures.

Bibliography

General

Byers, H. (1959). *General Meteorology* (3rd ed.), London/New York.
Compendium of Meteorology, (1951). American Meteorological Society, Boston.
Hann, J.-R. Süring, (1936–52). *Lehrbuch der Meteorologie*.
Hesse, W. (1961). *Handbuch der Aerologie*, Leipzig.
Huschke, R. E. (1959). *Glossary of Meteorology*, American Meteorological Society, Boston.
Keil, K. (1950). *Handwörterbuch der Meteorologie*, Frankfurt am Main.
Linke, F. and Baur, F. (1961). *Meteorologisches Taschenbuch* (new ed.), 2 vols., Leipzig.
Riehl, H. (1965). *Introduction to the Atmosphere*, London and New York.
Roll, H. U. (1965). *Physics of the Marine Atmosphere*, London and New York.
Roulleau, J. and Trochon, R. (1952–8). *Météorologie Générale*, 2 vols., Paris.
Schneider-Carius, K. (1955). *Wetterkunde und Wetterforschung*, Freiburg i. Br. and Munich.
Shaw, Sir Napier, (1928–36). *Manual of Meteorology*, 4 vols., Cambridge (Britain) and New York.
Smithsonian Meteorological Tables (6th ed.), (1958). Smithson. Miscell. Coll. 114, Washington.
U.S. Air Force Handbook of Geophysics and Space Environments. (1965). London and New York.

1 Radiation and the heat budget

Budyko, M. I. (1956). *Teplovoi Regime Zemnoi*, Leningrad.
Budyko, M. I. (1963). *Atlas Teplovevo Balansa Zemnovo Shara*, Leningrad.
Foitzik, L. and Hinzpeter, H. (1958). *Sonnenstrahlung und Lufttrübung*, Leipzig.
Geiger, R. (1961). *Das Klima der bodennahen Luftschicht*, Brunswick.
Goody, R. M. (1964). *Atmospheric Radiation*, vol. I, London and New York.
Lettau, H. H. and Davidson, B. (1957). *Exploring the Atmosphere's First Mile*, 2 vols., London and New York.
Linke, F. *et al.* (1951). *Handbuch der Geophysik*, vol. 8, Berlin.
London, J. (1957). *A Study of the Atmospheric Heat Balance*, University Dept. of Meteorological Oceanography, New York.

Möller, F. *et al.* (1957). *Handbuch der Geophysik*, vol. 48, Berlin.
Robinson, N. *et al.* (1966). *Solar Radiation*, Amsterdam.

2 Clouds and precipitation

Battan, L. J. (1959). *Radar Meteorology*, Cambridge (Britain) and Chicago.
Fletcher, N. H. (1962). *The Physics of Rainclouds*, Cambridge (Britain) and New York.
Ludlam, F. H. and Mason, B. J. (1957). *Handbuch der Geophysik*, vol. 48, Berlin.
Mason, B. J. (1957). *Physics of the Clouds*, Oxford and New York.
Mason, B. J. (1962). *Clouds, Rain and Rainmaking*, Cambridge (Britain) and New York.
Weickmann, H. (ed.), (1960). *Physics of Precipitation*, Amer. Geophys. Union, Geophys. Monog. 5., Washington.
World Meteorological Organisation. (1956). *International Cloud Atlas*, 2 vols., Geneva.

3 Atmospheric layers and circulation

Craig, R. A. (1956). *The Upper Atmosphere: Meteorology and Physics*, London and New York.
Defant, A. (1958). *Physikalische Dynamik der Atmosphere*, Frankfurt am Main.
Eliassen, A. and Kleinschmidt, E. (1957). *Handbuch der Geophysik*, vol. 48, Berlin.
Murgatroyd, R. J. *et al.* (1965). *The Circulation in the Stratosphere, Mesophere and Lower Thermosphere*, World. Meteor. Org., Tech. note 70.
Riehl, H. (1954). *Tropical Meteorology*, London and New York.
Schneider-Carius, K. (1953). *Die Grundschicht der Troposphäre*, Leipzig.
Willett, H. C. and Sanders, F. (1959). *Descriptive Meteorology* (2nd ed.), London and New York.

4 Weather annd weather forecasting

Dunn, G. E. and Miller, B. J. (1964). *Atlantic Hurricanes* (rev. ed.), Louisiana.
Kibel', I. A. (1963). *Hydrodynamical Methods of Short Period Weather Forecasting*, Oxford and New York.

247

Petterssen, Sverre (1957). *Weather Analysis and Forecasting* (2nd ed.), London and New York.

Reiter, E. R. (1963). *Jet-Stream Meteorology*, Chicago.

Reuter, H. (1954). *Methoden und Probleme der Wettervorhersage*, Vienna.

Scherhag, R. (1948). *Neue Methoden der Wetteranalyse und Wetterprognose*, Berlin.

Thompson, P. D. (1961). *Numerical Weather Analysis and Prediction*, London and New York.

Widger, W. K. (Jr.), (1966). *Meteorological Satellites*, New York.

5 Climate and climatic zones

Alissow, W. P., Drosdow, O. and Rubinstein, E. (1952). *Kurs Klimatologij*, Leningrad.

Blüthgen, J. (1964). *Allgemeine Klimageographie*, Berlin.

Heyer, E. (1963). *Witterung und Klima*, Leipzig.

Kendrew, W. G. (1961). *The Climates of the Continents* (5th ed.), London and New York.

Köppen, W. and Geiger, R. (1930–40). *Handbuch der Klimatologie*, 5 vols. (incomplete), Berlin.

Landsberg, H. E. *et al.*, (1965). *Weltkarten zur Klimakunde*, Berlin.

Meteorological Office, Tables of Temperature, *Relative Humidity and Precipitation for the World*, (1958). London.

Pédelaborde, P. (1958). *Les Moussons*, Paris.

Péguy, C. P. (1961). *Précis de Climatologie*, Paris.

Trewartha, G. T. (1961). *The Earth's Problem Climates*, Wisconsin and London.

World Meteorological Organisation (1962). *Climatological Normals* (CLINO) *for Climate and Climate Ship Stations for the Period* 1931–60, WMO-OMM, No. 117, TP 52.

World Weather Records, 5 vols., (1959, 1965), Smithson. Miscell. Coll. 79 (reprint 1944), 90 (1936), 105 (1947), U.S. Weather Bureau.

6 Climatic variations

Brooks, C. E. P. (1949). *Climate through the Ages* (2nd ed.), London and New York.

Nairn, A. E. M. (ed.), (1961). *Descriptive Palaeoclimatology*, London and New York.

Nairn, A. E. M. (ed.), (1964). *Problems in Palaeoclimatology*, London and New York.

Rudloff, H. von, (1966). *Die Schwankungen und Pendelungen des Klimas in Europa*, Brunswick.

Schwarzbach, M. (1961). *Das Klima der Vorzeit*, Stuttgart.

Shapley, H. (ed.), (1953). *Climatic Change*, Cambridge (Britain) and New York.

UNESCO-WMO, (1963). *Climatic Change*, Proceedings of the Rome Symposium, Paris.

Woldstedt, P. (1961–64). *Das Eiszeitalter*, 3 vols., Stuttgart.

7 Weather and climate modification

Flohn, H. (1963). *Klimaschwankungen und grossräunige Klimabeeinflussung*, Bonner Meteor. Abhandl. 2.

Gilman, D. L. *et al.*, (1965). *Weather and Climate Modification*, U.S. Dept. Commerce, Weather Bureau, Washington.

Junge, C. (1963). *Atmospheric Chemistry and Radioactivity*, London and New York.

Kratzer, A. (1956). *Das Stadklima*, Brunswick.

National Academy of Sciences, National Research Council (1965). *Weather and Climate Modifications*, 2 vols., Bull. Amer. Meteor. Soc. 47, 1966, pp. 1–20.

Schnelle, F. *et al.* (1963–5). *Frostschutz im Pflanzenbau*, 2 vols., Munich.

Smagorinsky, F. *et al. Monthly Weather Review*, vol. 91 (1963). pp. 99–163, vol. 93 (1965). pp. 727–98.

Weickmann, H. (ed.), (1957). *Artificial Stimulation of Rain*, London and New York.

Acknowledgments

Acknowledgment is due to the following for the photographs and diagrams (the numbers refer to the page on which the illustration appears).

14 modified from List (1958); 15 from Sellars in *Physical Climatology*, Univ. Chicago Press; 24–5 after Budyko (1963), based on map by courtesy Denoyer-Geppert Co., Chicago; 29, 46, 48 based on Trewartha in *The Elements of Climate*, McGraw-Hill; 50, 51, 54, 55, 58, 59, 62, 63, 66, 67, 71, 228 © Peter Smithson; 61, 64–5 © R. K. Pilsbury; 75 based on Mason in *Clouds, Rain and Rainmaking*, Cambridge University Press; 76–7 Crown copyright; 83, 126 based on Sutcliffe, *Weather and Climate*, Weidenfeld and Nicolson; 94, 130–1, 135 after Pedgley in *Elementary Meteorology*, HMSO; 102 based on Namias in Trewartha; 103 based on Hess; 112 after Sawyer; 122 modified from *Aviation Meteorology*, HMSO; 123 after Garnier in *Climate of New Zealand*, Arnold; 129, 132–3, 142 courtesy ESSA; 140 after Dunn and Miller, *Atlantic Hurricanes*, Louisiana State University Press; 144 courtesy German Weather Service; 146 modified from Widger in *Meteorological Satellites*, Holt, Rheinhart and Winston; 168, after Alpert in Trewartha, *The Earth's Problem Climates*, Methuen; 173 modified from Sawyer in *Q.J.R.M. Soc.* 1947; 183 after Trewartha in *The Earth's Problem Climates*, Methuen; 184 from Lamb in *Q.J.R. M. Soc.* 1959; 187 after Black 1954, Brown 1960, Frenzel 1959 and others in Butzer, *Environment and Archaeology*, Methuen; 197 (bottom) from Manley in *Climate and the British Scene*, Collins; 202 from Callandar in *Q.J.R.M. Soc.* 1961; 204 after Lamb, Probert-Jones and Sheard in *Journ. of Glaciology* (Cambridge) 1962; 211 data from J. R. Bray in *Nature*, vol. 209, p. 1065, 1967; 222–3 photo Claude Ronne ESSA; 226 based on Barrett in *I.B.G.*, vol. 35, 1964; 229 after Wilhelm Schmidt; 233 from *Tellus*, vol. 10, 1958.

The diagrams were drawn by Design Practitioners Limited.

Index

Numerals in **bold** refer to captions, illustrations, or both

252

World University Library

Books published or in preparation

Economics and Social Studies

The World Cities
Peter Hall, *London*

The Economics of Underdeveloped Countries
Jagdish Bhagwati, *MIT*

Development Planning
Jan Tinbergen, *Rotterdam*

Human Communication
J. L. Aranguren, *Madrid*

Education in the Modern World
John Vaizey, *London*

Money
Roger Opie, *Oxford*

Soviet Economics
Michael Kaser, *Oxford*

Decisive Forces in World Economics
J. L. Sampedro, *Madrid*

Key Issues in Criminology
Roger Hood, *Durham*

Population and History
E. A. Wrigley, *Cambridge*

History

The Emergence of Greek Democracy
W. G. Forrest, *Oxford*

Muhammad and the Conquests of Islam
Francesco Gabrieli, *Rome*

The Civilisation of Charlemagne
Jacques Boussard, *Poitiers*

The Crusades
Geo Widengren, *Uppsala*

The Ottoman Empire
Halil Inalcik, *Ankara*

Humanism in the Renaissance
S. Dresden, *Leyden*

The Rise of Toleration
Henry Kamen, *Warwick*

The Left in Europe
David Caute, *London*

The Rise of the Working Class
Jürgen Kuczynski, *Berlin*

Chinese Communism
Robert North, *Stanford*

The Italian City Republics
Daniel Waley, *London*

The Culture of Japan
Mifune Okumura, *Kyoto*

The History of Persia
Jean Aubin, *Paris*

A Short History of China
G. F. Hudson, *Oxford*

The Old Stone Age
François Bordes, *Bordeaux*

The Arts

The Language of Modern Art
Ulf Linde, *Stockholm*

Twentieth Century Music
H. H. Stuckenschmidt, *Berlin*

Art Nouveau
S. Tschudi Madsen, *Oslo*

Palaeolithic Cave Art
P. J. Ucko and A. Rosenfeld, *London*

Primitive Art
Eike Haberland, *Mainz*

Expressionism
John Willett, *London*

Language and Literature

French Literature
Raymond Picard, *Paris*

**Russian Writers and Society
1825–1904**
Ronald Hingley, *Oxford*

Satire
Matthew Hodgart, *Sussex*

The Romantic Century
Robert Baldick, *Oxford*

Philosophy and Religion

Christian Monasticism
David Knowles, *London*

Witchcraft
Lucy Mair, *London*

Sects
Bryan Wilson, *Oxford*

Earth Sciences and Astronomy

The Structure of the Universe
E. L. Schatzman, *Paris*

Anatomy of the Earth
André Cailleux, *Paris*

Sun, Earth and Radio
J. A. Ratcliffe, *Cambridge*

Zoology and Botany

Mimicry in plants and animals
Wolfgang Wickler, *Seewiesen*

Lower Animals
Martin Wells, *Cambridge*

The World of an Insect
Rémy Chauvin, *Strasbourg*

Primates
François Bourlière, *Paris*

The Age of the Dinosaurs
Björn Kurtén, *Helsinki*

Psychology and Human Biology

Eye and Brain
R. L. Gregory, *Edinburgh*

The Ear and the Brain
E. C. Carterette, *UCLA*

The Biology of Work
O. G. Edholm, *London*

**The Psychology of Fear
and Stress**
J. A. Gray, *Oxford*

The Tasks of Childhood
Philippe Muller, *Neuchâtel*

The Doctor and the Patient
P. Lain Entralgo, *Madrid*

Physical Science and Mathematics

The Quest for Absolute Zero
K. Mendelssohn, *Oxford*

What is Light ?
A. C. S. van Heel and
C. H. F. Velzel, *Eindhoven*

Mathematics Observed
Hans Freudenthal, *Utrecht*

Waves and Corpuscles
J. Andrade e Silva and G. Lochak,
Paris Introduction by Louis de Broglie

Particles and Accelerators
Robert Gouiran, *Geneva*

Applied Science

Words and Waves
A. H. W. Beck, *Cambridge*

The Science of Decision-making
A. Kaufmann, *Paris*

Bionics
Lucien Gérardin, *Paris*

Data Study
J. L. Jolley, *London*